Insects

Richard Jones

Collins

This book is for my parents. My father, Alfred Jones, from whom I acquired my love of natural history, gave me a precious gift – the thirst for knowledge. My mother, Rosamond Jones, gave me the time and her tolerance, whilst I tried to quench it.

HarperCollins Publishers

77-85 Fulham Palace Road

London W6 8JB

www.harpercollins.co.uk

Collins is a registered trademark of HarperCollins Publishers Ltd.

First published in 2010

This paperback edition published in 2011

16 15 14 13 12 11

10 9 8 7 6 5 4 3 2 1

ISBN 978 0 00 739356 5

Edited and designed by Tall Tree Ltd

Editor: Rob Colson

Designer: Jonathan Vipond

Cover design: Greg Whyte

Colour reproduction by Dot Gradations Ltd, UK

Printed and bound in China

Acknowledgements

Early inspiration for the entries in this book came from the topics and approach of previous titles in the series: *Extreme Nature* by Mark Carwardine and *Extreme Birds* by Dominic Couzens. An important source of information on insect records can be found in the University of Florida Book of Insect Records (http://ufbir.ifas.ufl.edu/), which has long erudite discussions on various insect records and the problems of measuring them.

Many people have come up with ideas for this book. At a very early stage my daughters Lillian and Verity Ure-Jones came up with some novel and entertaining proposals including shiniest, spikiest and ugliest, which are here; and also kindest, cleverest and grumpiest, which would have been fun, but never made it through the vetting process. I also had a brainstorming session with the Natural History Club at Ivydale Primary School, who came up with most beautiful, most irritating and slimiest, all of which are here.

Finally, thank you to Max Barclay at the Natural History Museum for getting hold of copies of some obscure reference articles, and water beetle experts David Bilton and Garth Foster who both independently came up with the suggestion for rarest insect, a water beetle.

Richard Jones

Contents

6 Introduction

8 Extreme Form

116 Extreme Evolution

214 Extreme Impact

284 Index

Introduction

Insects are the most extreme organisms on Earth, and despite their diminutive stature, they wield inordinate power. With the exception of the polar ice caps, every terrestrial ecosystem on Earth is colonised by insects and to some extent controlled by them (and they have made inroads onto the open ocean, too). They dominate the middle ground of virtually every terrestrial food chain or food web.

Insects are extreme in numbers. A single leaf-cutter ant nest, the size of a large camper van buried in the soil, may contain 8 million individuals working together as a single giant super-organism. In the tropical rainforests, termites can reach densities of 10,000 per square metre, a higher density of animal mass than in the largest wildebeest herds of the Serengeti. To produce such numbers, insects are extreme in their fecundity. Egg loads can be counted in thousands and generation times in days. If conditions are right, plagues of biblical proportions can appear as if spontaneously.

Insects are extreme in diversity. Even the experts cannot agree whether there are 3 million different species of insect on the Earth, 10 million, 30 million or 80 million. Compare that to the mere 5,400 known species of mammal. About four-fifths of all the animals yet discovered on our planet are insects: that's over 1 million species at the last count. And there are many times that number out there awaiting discovery.

Insects are extreme in form. Evolved into the most peculiar shapes and colours, with strange structures and beautiful patterns, even the smallest of these wonderful creatures is magnificent under the microscope. Each has adapted to solve the extreme pressures that arise in the struggle to survive in a world that is dangerous, competitive and unforgiving.

Extreme Insects is divided into three chapters, exploring the nature of the insect universe and looking at some of the most extraordinary creatures in existence.

Extreme Form. In addition to the biggest, smallest, and largest wingspan, we take a look at extreme shapes: spikiest, furriest, shiniest, flattest. Why have such forms evolved? What benefit do they give to the insects that possess them?

Extreme Evolution. Some parts of insect anatomy can appear completely alien to the human eye. They have evolved to allow their possessors a special tool, weapon or means of escape. They have allowed certain insects to survive in extremely difficult or dangerous circumstances. Insects are complex creatures that interact with each other, with their food and with enemies who see them as food. And they get up to some very strange things. They seem to be dancing, skulking or hiding. They brave danger or run like cowards. Some nurture and some murder; some commit suicide. They may appear very clever or extremely dim. Some steal and some give gifts. What is the biological explanation behind these apparently odd behaviours?

Extreme Impact. Humans now reckon themselves to be the dominant life form on Earth, but we have been around for only a few hundred thousand years. Insects were here over 300 million years earlier. Humans, the mere junior upstarts, now come into conflict with a much older and better-established group of organisms. And despite our modern sophistication, we cannot escape such tenacious and apparently determined animals. They invade our fields, our houses and even our bodies. Some we can tame for our own uses, but with others we are still at war.

Insects are both awful and awe-inspiring, certainly worthy of our respect and our study. They give us a window on the natural world through which we can see, and attempt to understand, the environment in which we live, indeed of which we are an integral part. The huge numbers of insects, and their depredations on human food and health, are sometimes bemoaned. In reality, they form a vast biomass, and it is a wasteful shame that insects form an insignificant part of the human diet. We may not eat them very often, but insects offer a more philosophical sustenance – food for thought. In their study, there is a veritable feast for the mind.

Richard Jones
London, September 2009

Extreme

Form

Oldest insect · Biggest insect · Longest insect · Whitest insect · Shiniest insect · Slimiest insect · Biggest blockhead · Most sexually dimorphic insect · Most mixed-up sexuality · Most bloated insect · Most seasonally dimorphic insect · Highest number of wings · Flattest insect · Most back-to-front insect · Longest ovipositor · Widest head · Brightest light generation · Most variable colour pattern · Bloodiest insect · Most beautiful insect · Longest head · Most streamlined insect · Loudest insect · Best hoverer · Ugliest insect · Largest jaws · Largest wingspan · Best camouflage · Most transparent wings · Hairiest legs · Snappiest jaws · Prettiest eyes · Most elegant eggs · Largest eye markings · Lightest footstep · Furriest insect · Most poisonous insect · Most heavily armoured insect · Longest wing tails · Best burrower · Smallest insect · Heaviest insect · Fastest flier · Fastest runner · Longest tongue · Smelliest insect · Most subterranean insect · Fastest wing-beat · Smallest egg · Largest egg · Spikiest insect · Biggest feet · Largest claws

Oldest insect

NAME *Rhyniognatha hirsti*

LOCATION fossil discovered in Aberdeenshire, Scotland

STATUS oldest known fossil of an insect

Most insects are very small, very delicate and very edible, so the fossil record they have left behind is extremely poor. The majority end up as prey for other animals, bitten, chewed and digested away. Where their remains are not eaten, there are no large bones to be preserved, and even the toughest of insect shells are made of highly biodegradable compounds. As a result, it takes some pretty special circumstances for insect fossils to form, and they are thoroughly scrutinised when found. Or at least they should be.

Until recently, the oldest acknowledged insect-like fossil was an ancient relative of modern springtails. These are wingless soft-bodied creatures that are not now classed as insects but as a sister group within the subphylum *Hexapoda* (six-legged arthropods). The fossil was found in 1919 by the Reverend W. Cran in the old red sandstone deposits (also called the Rhynie cherts) at Rhynie in Aberdeenshire, Scotland, which date from 407–396 million years ago. It was finally described in 1926 by three paleontologists, S. Hirst, S. Maulik and D.J. Scourfield, who aptly named it *Rhyniella praecursor*.

Two years later the rock sample was re-examined by the Australian entomologist Robin Tillyard. He identified what had been thought to be a broken fragment of a *Rhyniella* head capsule as belonging to a different creature, which he named *Rhyniognatha hirsti*.

The specimen lay untouched in the Natural History Museum, London, until 2004, when it was examined again by evolutionary entomologists Michael Engel and David Grimaldi. Using modern microscopes, they were able to see the fossilised jaws in much greater detail, and made an astonishing discovery. The shape of the jaws – toothed, broadly triangular, with two bulges where they articulated against other sections of the mouthparts – showed that they were not from some ancient springtail, but from a true insect and probably one with wings.

The Rhynie cherts formed in an area of hot springs and active geysers, which contained fluids rich in dissolved silica. As the water cooled the silica crystallised out of the water to form the fossils for which the area is now renowned. Hot water is very damaging to insect wings and other soft tissues, so it is not surprising that only the tough jaws of this insect have been preserved.

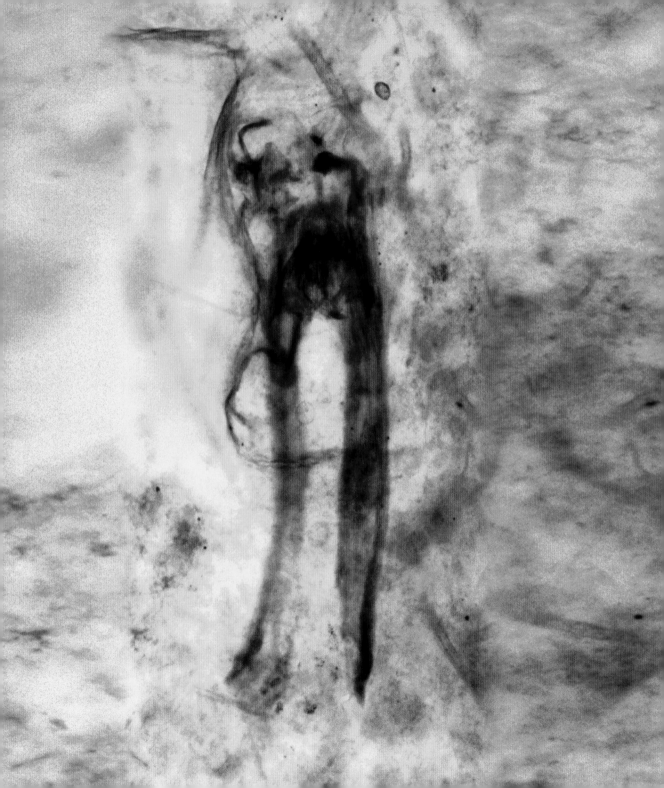

In 1771, the Swedish naturalist Carolus Linnaeus described a giant beetle, and named it using his new scheme of binomial (two names) nomenclature: one name for the genus (*Titanus*) and one name for the species (*giganteus*). This name could not have been more apt for an insect that regularly reaches 17 cm (6.7 in) long. Linnaeus never saw the beetle itself. He coined the name after seeing an engraving of it in an encyclopedia.

The reason Linnaeus never saw one is that this was one of the rarest insects then known. During the 18th century, specimens were occasionally washed up dead on the shores of the Rio Negro, near Manaos in Brazil. The first living beetles were not found until 1958, when they were attracted to the street lights which were newly installed in the towns and villages in the area. Its early stages and life history are still unknown, but similar species have maggot-like larvae that feed in rotten logs.

There is still some doubt as to whether *Titanus giganteus* truly is the 'largest' insect. Few reliable measurements of living specimens have been taken. There is also little data regarding its weight – usually regarded as the key indicator of size by record-measuring organisations. As a result, four other beetles are contenders for the title. These are the shorter but stouter 'Elephant' beetles from South America – *Megasoma actaeon* (13.5 cm) and *M. elephas* (13.7 cm) – and the Goliath beetles from Africa – *Goliathus regius* (11 cm) and *G. goliathus* (11 cm).

Biggest insect

NAME	*Titanus giganteus*
LOCATION	Venezuela, Colombia, Ecuador, Peru, the Guianas, Brazil
ATTRIBUTE	largest living insect

One of the best ways to avoid being eaten is to hide, and one of the best ways to hide is to blend in with the surroundings using camouflage. Stick insects (also called walking sticks) have taken this to an extreme, and their pencil-thin bodies and pin-thin legs perfectly resemble the twigs through which they climb. So good at hiding have they become that some stick insects have acquired a trait that is a common evolutionary result of having no (or virtually no) predators – they have become very large.

For nearly 100 years, the record for the longest insect in the world was held by a specimen of a giant stick insect from Borneo, *Phobaeticus* (formerly *Pharnacia*) *kirbyi*. Its body was 328 mm (12.9 in) long, and from the tip of the outstretched front leg to the end of the back leg it measured 499 mm (19.6 in). This specimen had long been misidentified as the closely related *P. serratipes*, and it was only shortly after its true identity was established in 1995 that another huge stick insect was discovered. Ironically, this time it was a specimen of the true *P. serratipes*, found in Malaysia. It had a total length of 555 mm (21.9 in), although its body alone was slightly shorter than the famous *P. kirbyi* specimen.

Measuring lanky insects is fraught with difficulties, and this could have been the point at which some controversy arose. Most size measurements for insects deliberately ignore legs, antennae, tails and snouts because they vary tremendously within a population, especially between male and female of the same species. It has long been known that the leg lengths of stick insects vary, even when measured on different sides of the same specimen. However, the matter was settled in October 2008, with the description of a new species of stick insect from the Malaysian state of Sabah on the island of Borneo. *Phobaeticus chani* was named after the entomologist Datuk Chan Chew Lun, who donated the largest of three specimens, found by a local collector, to the Natural History Museum in London. With a body length of 357 mm (14 in) and a total length of 566 mm (22.3 in), it takes the record no matter which way it is measured.

Longest insect

NAME *Phobaeticus chani*
LOCATION Borneo
ATTRIBUTE greatest length in body and legs of any insect

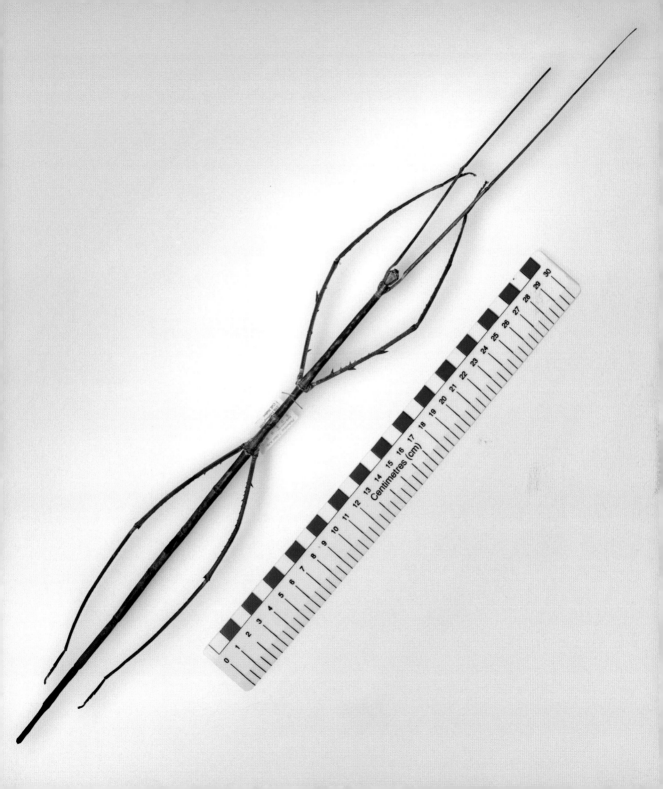

Whitest insect

NAME **Ghost beetles** in the genus *Cyphochilus*
LOCATION Southeast Asia
ATTRIBUTE the whitest covering of any insect

White is not a common insect colour, as it makes an insect stand out to predators in a natural world dominated by browns and greens. Perhaps the best-known white insects are cabbage whites (*Pieris* species). Like other butterflies, they use their colour patterns to recognise each other when mating. But they fade into insignificance against ghost beetles in the genus *Cyphochilus*.

Ghost beetles are found throughout Southeast Asia, where they are sometimes regarded as a pest in sugar cane plantations. Ghost beetle larvae feed in fungi, and the beetles' whiteness is thought to be a camouflage against this rare white foodstuff. On close examination, the whiteness is caused not by the beetle's exoskeleton (its tough outer shell-like body), which is dark brown and almost black, but by a dusty coating of pure white overlapping scales, which cover its body, head and legs. Each scale is minute, measuring only 250 by 100 µm and just 5 µm thick (a µm or micrometre is one thousandth of a millimetre).

The scales were first studied by Pete Vukusic, an optical physicist at Exeter University in the UK, who discovered that the beetles' whiteness is caused by a random network of tiny filaments, 0.25 µm in diameter, inside the scale. The random arrangement of the filaments means that the different rainbow colours in natural white light are scattered simultaneously, equally and highly efficiently, with no single colour predominating . The beetles are among the whitest objects found in nature – much whiter than teeth and milk.

Shiniest insect

NAME	**golden chafers** in the genus *Plusiotis*
LOCATION	Central and South America
ATTRIBUTE	appear to be wrought from burnished gold and silver

Insect colours serve many purposes. Greens and browns act as camouflage against living and dead leaves, tree trunks, branches and twigs. Bright yellow, orange and red, often marked with black, warn that an individual is poisonous or might sting. But the brightest and most spectacular colours do neither. Metallic glints of bronze, blue, green, red and violet occur in many beetles, bees, wasps, flies and, of course, butterflies (see page 48). The most astonishing of these are the brilliantly shining golden chafers, *Plusiotis* species, of Central and South America.

Metallic sheens are not colours in the conventional sense of a pigment or colourant on the surface of the animal. The red of a ladybird, for instance, appears because the yellow, green and blue wavelengths in sunlight are absorbed and only red light reflects back into the eye of the beholder. The metallic shine of the golden chafers, by contrast, is caused by the white sunlight being broken, much as it is when shining through a diamond, to give a series of rainbow glints.

Seen through an electron microscope, the surface of the beetle is revealed to be covered with minute parallel grooves. These reflect certain portions of the light at the precise angle to shine like polished metal, while absorbing and scattering other wavelengths.

Shining colours are not just for showing off to a potential mate, although this is important for many butterflies. One of the main purposes, ironically, may be to avoid attention. In bright sunlight, against wet mud or in the dripping rainforest canopy, metallic glints are surprisingly confusing to the eye of a predator, which searches for images based on shape.

Slimiest insect

NAME **fungus gnat larvae** in the family Keroplatidae
LOCATION worldwide
ATTRIBUTE create mucus webs to collect their food

Contrary to popular opinion, insects (like snakes) are not slimy. Slime or, to give it its more technical term, mucus, is a sticky secretion used especially by molluscs and vertebrates. Snails and slugs use it to lubricate their path as they glide forwards on their own moist layer, and to a certain extent as a defence, since the stickiness deters predators, which can get gummed up in it. Vertebrates use it to line their airways, guts and genital tract, and to cover their eyes, where it forms a gel layer in which antiseptic enzymes can protect against microbial attack. Mucus is a very sticky substance, and very useful, so it will come as no surprise to learn that some insects use it after all.

Mucus is made up of mucin molecules – a number of long protein chains covered with atomic groups which resemble sugar molecules. The sugar parts (glycans) attract water (and each other) and as the long mucin molecules slide past one another, these areas act like weak glue, partly sticking the strands together. The mucus remains wet and tacky, and does not set hard like that other important long-chain protein molecule, silk, which is produced from the salivary glands of many insect larvae, which use it to spin a cocoon in which to become adult.

Fungus gnat larvae produce mucus from their salivary glands, but they do this throughout their larvahood, not just during metamorphosis at the end. The larvae of these small midge-like flies live under dead logs, fungal fruiting bodies or in caves. Here they build a rough sheet web of sticky mucus strands, covered all over in tiny water droplets. Sometimes they add a soft flexible tube into which they retreat for shelter. Many species eat highly nutritious fungal spores. The spores are impossible to catch when airborne but are caught in the gleaming mucus, and can then be eaten. The webs of some species also contain oxalic acid, a simple chemical similar to vinegar but much more powerful. It is highly toxic to many animals (including humans), and the gnat larvae use it to kill insect prey, which they then eat too.

Ants gain protection from a complex social hierarchy that generates workers to forage and build, and soldiers to fight and protect. The nest that they build and protect is the ants' most important asset. Ants need to protect their nest from many enemies, including predators, parasites and other ants who would like to raid the valuable protein invested in the brood as well as any food stores laid up against hard times.

Soldier carpenter ants have evolved huge mallet-shaped heads with which to bar their nest entrances. Small holes are blocked by a single soldier, while for larger entrances several soldiers gather together to form a living barricade. The soldiers seldom leave the nest, but are fed by the workers that constantly come and go.

When a worker needs to exit or enter the nest (see opposite), it is recognised by the blocking soldier, which pulls back into the broader tunnel behind. It is thought a combination of the host nest's chemical smells and the 'right' tactile signals from the worker's antennae identify it as a fellow citizen. If there is an attack on the colony, alerted ants release a chemical called undecane from a gland in their abdomen. This creates rapid excitement of other ants, and the many soldiers rush to block all external and internal tunnels.

Biggest blockhead

NAME   **carpenter ants** *Colobopsis truncatus* (and other species)

LOCATION   worldwide

ABILITY   uses its head as a living gate at the entrance to its burrow

Most sexually dimorphic insect

NAME   **European snail beetle**   *Drilus flavescens*
LOCATION   mainland Europe and the UK
ATTRIBUTE   most extreme difference between male and female

Males and females are different. Males produce huge amounts of tiny sperm, which they generally try to spread about between as many females as they can. Females carry the eggs, and although they may benefit from males competing for their attentions, multiple matings carry a cost in terms of time wasted and sometimes even physical damage. These different biological drives often produce very different behaviours in male and female of the same species, and sometimes also different body forms. In most insects these structural differences are small, but in one group of beetles, males and females are so different that they look like completely different organisms.

The European snail beetle, *Drilus flavescens*, is small (4 to 7 mm) and brown; it has a black head and thorax, and feathery antennae – at least the male has. The female, by extreme contrast, is a large, soft, flabby, caterpillar-like creature, 50 times as large as the male. The males fly on hot sunny days, but the females lack both the normal hard beetle wingcases and also the functional membranous flight wings. The distribution of the males shows that the species is fairly widespread on limestone or chalk soils, but despite this the female is virtually unknown. In fact, the female of this peculiar species is so rarely seen that there was no reliable published picture of her until this mating pair was photographed in 2003.

The larvae of *Drilus* eat small snails. Despite being a widespread insect, the rarity (or perhaps the secretiveness) of the females and larvae meant that the beetle's life cycle was not worked out until 1903. Quite why males and females of *Drilus* should be so very different is still a bit of a mystery, although many female glow-worms (also beetles but in a completely different family) are also wingless, and their larvae, too, are snail predators.

Most mixed-up sexuality

Insects are usually either wholly male or wholly female. In extremely rare situations, however, there appears an individual that is exactly half one sex and half the other – a bilateral gynandromorph – and nowhere is this more striking than when it involves a butterfly. In butterflies, as in most animals, sex is determined by the chromosomes. Females have two X chromosomes (XX) and males have just one (XO). Butterfly sperm contains either an X or no sex chromosome.

In this marsh fritillary butterfly (*Euphydryas aurinia*) the sperm that originally fertilised the egg contained an X chromosome so the offspring was due to be XX, female. But after the very first cell division into two, one of the XX cells (female) somehow lost an X and became XO (male). Throughout the many millions of further cell divisions in the growing caterpillar and during metamorphosis in the chrysalis the right-hand side of the insect stayed female while the left-hand side had become male. When the final adult butterfly emerged from its pupa, it continued to be right half female and left half male.

Gynandromorphs are very rare and unlikely to survive. Neither male nor female sexual organs are functional. Some striking butterfly specimens occur where males and females have different wing patterns. In the case of the marsh fritillary, males are significantly smaller than females. This specimen was reared as part of a genetic study. In the wild all it could have achieved in life would have been a terminal spiral flight.

NAME **bilateral gynandromorph** various species, but particularly prominent in butterflies
LOCATION this example was bred in captivity
ATTRIBUTE half male and half female

For most aboriginal peoples, honey from bees was the only source of sweetness for thousands of years. But in Australia, western USA, Mexico, South Africa and New Guinea, they could raid another source – the hugely bloated honeypot ants.

Honeypot ants have grossly distended abdomens. Their job is to hang immobile from the roofs of nest burrows and fill up with the goodies brought back by their nest-mates, the workers – nectar and honeydew (aphid excrement little changed from the liquid plant sap these insects suck out). This behaviour has evolved in several different genera around the world, usually in desert habitats where the storage of food against hard times allows the colony to survive in the harshest of environments.

The storage ants, called 'repletes', can expand their bodies by a factor of many hundreds compared to the normal workers. Their translucent bodies vary in colour from almost clear, through yellow-brown to dark amber. The darker bodies contain the sugars glucose and fructose. The palest and heaviest repletes contain very dilute sugar solutions.

The evolution of repletes is thought to be linked to a system that exploits the unpredictable food sources provided by desert flowers. The volume of the repletes is built up in cool, moist weather, and they are then tapped by the rest of the colony during hot, dry times. The change from building up to tapping happens at about 30–31°C (86–88°F), suggesting that the real purpose of the repletes is to store water against drought.

Most bloated insect

NAME **honeypot ants** *Myrmecocystus* species, *Camponotus inflatus* and others
LOCATION Australia, New Guinea, South Africa, western USA to Mexico
ABILITY use their stretched bodies to store sugar and water

Most seasonally dimorphic insect

NAME   **map butterfly** *Araschnia levana*

LOCATION   widespread across mainland Europe

ATTRIBUTE   alternating generations of completely different-looking butterflies

The European map butterfly, *Araschnia levana*, gets its name from the pretty patterns that mark the undersides of its wings. The mottled browns and oranges of its background are criss-crossed with bright white lines reminiscent of the radiating compass marks superimposed on old maps and nautical charts. However, it is the patterns of the upper sides that are most remarkable.

Spring butterflies, emerging from chrysalises that have remained dormant through winter, are bright orange above, marked with a series of black spots and blotches. Their eggs produce caterpillars that feed quickly on their nettle host-plants, and the summer generation of butterflies that emerges a few weeks later has a completely different colour pattern – jet black, with a strong white flash down each wing (shown right). So different are these colour forms that they were long thought to be two distinct species.

This extreme dimorphism (meaning 'two forms') has attracted a lot of research from entomologists, and the factors that decide which colour pattern will be produced are now well understood. The final adult morph is decided by the effects of day length and temperature on the feeding caterpillar. Short days and cold, enough to induce winter torpor, produce the spring orange form *levana* while long hot days produce the black and white summer form *prorsa*. Experiments have shown that caterpillars from either generation can be raised under artificially altered temperature and daylight regimes to produce the 'wrong' adults.

It is still not known why the map butterfly shows such stark changes between its two generations. The scene is further confused by the fact that more northerly and montane populations have only one generation (form *levana*) each year, while in the south there is a partial third generation with intermediate *levana/prorsa* characters.

As well as different colour patterns, the summer form *prorsa* has larger and less pointed wings, a heavier (presumably more muscular) thorax and relatively smaller abdomen. These characters fit the idea that the summer form is better at migrating to colonise new regions (the spring form is noticeably more sedentary), but it still does not explain why one butterfly species should look like two completely different creatures.

Adult insects usually have two pairs of wings. Some groups have fewer: flies have only one pair; lice and fleas have none at all. Even beetles, which might look as if they have none at first, still have four wings; two are developed into the hard shell wing-cases, and cover the delicately folded flight wings underneath. But could this be a moth with twenty wings?

Plume moths have long, narrow, hairy wings that resemble birds' feathers. At rest they fold their wings up tightly to resemble twigs and dead grass stems. In some species the wings are split into hairy fingers, each finger acting as a structural vein to expand the narrow wings into a broader aerofoil in flight. The greatest splitting occurs in the twenty-plume moths, where each of the four 'true' wings is divided right down to the base into a fan of finger-wings. Whoever named the moth miscounted. In fact, it has 24 plumes.

The plumes of these moths are analogous to the veins that spread through all insect wings. The veins are most obvious in clear-winged insects such as bees, wasps and flies. Insect wings are thought to have evolved from broad flap-like appendages used as gills by their aquatic predecessors, and the veins are the vestiges of breathing tubes. Such gill flaps are still visible today in the larvae of stoneflies (Plecoptera) and mayflies (Ephemeroptera).

Insects are thought to have evolved wings only once, about 400 million years ago. After examining the different wing structures, scientists now believe that the first truly flapping and flying insects had eight veins in each wing. Over evolutionary time these have often become merged with each other or reduced to six main veins. These six archetypal veins are clearly seen in *Alucita*.

Highest number of wings

NAME	**twenty-plumed moths** in the genus *Alucita*
LOCATION	worldwide
ATTRIBUTE	more wings than any other insects

Flattest insect

NAME	**violin beetles** in the genus *Mormolyce*
LOCATION	Southeast Asia
ATTRIBUTE	most flattened insect form

Ground beetles (family Carabidae) are, as their name suggests, usually found running about on the ground, where they hunt small insects and other invertebrate prey. They are found throughout the world and are one of the most diverse and successful groups of insects. Their success is due in part to a peculiar structure near the base of each of their hind legs. The trochanter is a small muscle-filled lobe where the femur (thigh) joins the coxa (hip). It gives the long back legs extra strength, not just to push backwards, but to push downwards at the same time.

Ground beetles use this ability in a technique called wedge-pushing to squeeze into a tight space in the roots of grass or through the soil under a stone. First the beetle pushes its wedge-shaped body forwards as far as it can go, then it levers itself up and down to press back the herbage or soil slightly so it can push forwards again. Using this unique semi-subterranean propulsion method, ground beetles are able to pursue their prey farther and deeper into the dense thatch of plant roots and leaf litter.

The violin beetles – of which five species are known, all from Southeast Asia – have taken this squeezing habit to a bizarre conclusion. Rather than thrusting themselves through the undergrowth, they have chosen another, equally tight, spot in which to hunt: in the narrow crevices beneath the loose bark of dead trees, stumps and logs. As well as an extremely flattened body, violin beetles have a narrow head and thorax to examine minute cracks in the dead timber. They also explore cracks in the earth and the axils of bromeliads.

Most back-to-front insect

NAME	**apple leaf-miner moth** *Lyonetia clerkella*
LOCATION	Western Europe
ATTRIBUTE	appears to have legs, eyes and antennae at the tips of its wings

Apple, pear and cherry leaves are prone to attack from the caterpillars of a tiny moth. The caterpillars are so small that rather than eat the leaves from the outside, they burrow along inside them, leaving a winding, pale, air-filled space behind. But what is most remarkable about this insect is that when the adult moth emerges it appears to have its head at the wrong end. Careful inspection of the moth's tiny 4-mm wings shows that they are entirely white apart from the grey and black marks at their tips. The pattern of dark scales against white is clearly arranged to look like a separate miniature insect, with dark body outline, six legs, two short antennae and two round black eyes.

False eyes, heads and antennae are quite common in butterflies, with many species having prominent dark eye spots at the hind wing edges alongside short or long tails which resemble antennae. Swallowtails unsurprisingly have tails, as do many hairstreaks and blues. *Lyonetia* is one of a range of micromoths with false legs and heads at the tips of the wings. Some leafhopper bugs, which also have wings folded tent-like over the abdomen, have similar patterns.

Until recently, the conventional wisdom was that false heads attracted the attentions of predators to bite at the relatively expendable wing extremities, preventing fatal damage to the vital organs. However, an intriguing theory suggests that rather than attracting bites to the 'wrong' end, the false head at the tail encourages attack on the true head. A predator seeing the moth might reasonably feel its best chance is to sneak up from behind, but it will in reality be making a frontal advance on the insect's real head, where it is more likely to be detected by the moth's real eyes and real antennae.

Longest ovipositor (egg-laying tube)

Ichneumons are related to wasps, but instead of building nests for their larvae, they choose a more insidious lifestyle for their young. Ichneumons lay their eggs in the bodies of other insects, usually moth and butterfly caterpillars, but also insect eggs or pupae. The hatching maggot then eats the host animal alive, from the inside, eventually killing it. An organism that lives on or in a host and kills it in this way is known as a parasitoid.

Together with the many other parasitic 'wasps', ichneumons are a large and diverse group of creatures, which target a huge range of insect hosts. At one end of the scale are some of the smallest insects known (see page 90); at the other end are the giant ichneumon or sabre wasps in the genus *Rhyssa*.

Giant ichneumons need a host animal of suitable size to feed their equally giant larvae, and choose the larvae of another group of very large insects – the horntails. Horntails (*Syrex* species) are huge hornet-sized insects, named after their own large, stout tails, which they use to saw into fallen logs and rotten tree trunks to deposit their eggs. Their large grubs will chew burrows through the dead wood for between one and three years before finally emerging as adults.

Rhyssa females are able to detect chemicals given off by the *Syrex* larva, even through 4 cm (1¼ in) of wood. The narrow 4 cm tail of a sabre wasp, usually longer than the rest of her body, is composed of three pieces – two thick outer strips form a protective sheath that covers the needle-thin ovipositor (egg-laying tube). Using her long legs and flexible abdomen as a gantry, she slowly pushes the slim egg tube down through the timber until she is able to parasitise the grub below. Her offspring is now assured of food to see it through to adulthood, but the horntail maggot is doomed.

NAME	**sabre ichneumon** in the genus *Rhyssa*
LOCATION	Europe, North Africa, Asia, North America
ATTRIBUTE	hypodermic-like egg-laying tube longer than the rest of its body

It is a sad fact of life that males often fight each other for the attentions of females. The prize for the victor may be a harem and numerous offspring, but the cost in energy expenditure and bodily damage may be high, and life expectancy short. It is better to be able to size up an opponent before falling to blows, and stalk-eyed flies do this eye-ball to eye-ball.

Many groups of small tropical flies have broad heads, and this is taken to extremes in the family *Diopsidae*. More than 150 species in this family have heads so wide that the eyes are held out on unfeasibly long, thin horizontal stalks. Very often the head width (12–14 mm) is twice the length of the fly's body (6–7 mm). Head width, or rather eye-stalk length, is directly proportional to body size, and a good indicator of body strength, which itself is directly linked to the fly's nutrition when it was a larva. Male diopsids face off in a head-to-head stalk-measuring contest. The winner gets the females, but the loser walks away unharmed.

This ritual behaviour is thought to have evolved because these tropical flies are relatively long-lived (12 months has been recorded), and because they have something important to guard. Other groups of small flies with shorter lifespans and narrower (but still relatively stout) heads actually come to head-butting bouts: they have little to lose so they just go for it. Male diopsids, on the other hand, have been observed repeatedly contesting for 200 consecutive days.

The valuable resources that male diopsids are defending are string-thin rootlets hanging down from the banks of small streams that run through the woodland in which they live. These apparently mundane bits of straggling vegetation are the prime night-roosting sites for large numbers of females. They gather here and all face upwards, the direction from which any potential predator will come. By fighting, or at least flaunting his broad head, a male diopsid rules the roost and secures his harem.

Widest head

NAME	**stalk-eyed flies** in the family Diopsidae
LOCATION	throughout the tropics, particularly Southeast Asia and Southern Africa
ATTRIBUTE	eyes on thin stalks longer than their bodies

Brightest light generation

NAME **Jamaican fire beetle** *Pyrophorus noctilucus*
LOCATION Central and South America
ATTRIBUTE brightest light production by any insect

Several groups of insects can generate light, including the springtails, true bugs, fly larvae and especially the beetles. The well-known glow-worms and fireflies are neither worms nor flies, but beetles, and many species occur worldwide. Light-generating beetles use their lights to attract or communicate with potential mates. Some flash to a secret rhythm, while others emit a continuous pale glow. There has long been debate about which beetle species might be brightest and until recently comparisons were rather subjective, usually describing the similarity to a candle at some set distance as seen by the naked eye or to stars of various brightnesses. Supremely accurate photometers can now measure light production down to the atomic level, and a clear winner has been found – *Pyrophorus noctilucus*, a click beetle found in forests in the West Indies.

It is auspicious that this species should rank highest. In 1885 the French physiologist Raphael Dubois first isolated the compounds luciferin and luciferase by dissecting the glowing spots on the thorax of

P. noctilucus. Similar chemicals are found in all light-emitting organisms. Light generation by living organisms (known as bioluminescence) is remarkable because it is 'cold'. Using the old candle analogy, a firefly produces 1/80,000th of the heat that would be created by a candle of the same brightness.

The chemical reactions that produce light are based on the enzyme luciferase, which combines luciferin with oxygen and adenosine triphosphate (ATP). The significance of Dubois's discovery was not fully understood for nearly 60 years until ATP was identified as the energy-carrying molecular currency in every living thing. In photosynthesis, light energy is captured by green plants and transformed into chemical energy in the form of ATP. This is used to make basic sugars and other substances from carbon dioxide in the atmosphere and water taken up by the roots. Photosynthesis absorbs light; bioluminescence releases light. The two reactions are equal, but the reverse of each other.

Naming plants and animals should be a relatively straightforward procedure. Since the Swedish naturalist Karl von Linné (also Latinised to Carolus Linnaeus) developed the binomial (two-name) system, each organism has been given two names. Thus, for the seven-spot ladybird we have one name for the genus, *Coccinella*, meaning ladybird, and one for the particular species, *septempunctata*, meaning seven-spotted.

Except that nothing in nature is that straightforward. The common seven-spot always has seven spots, but the closely related ten-spot ladybird, *Adalia decempunctata*, very rarely has ten. In fact it can have anything down to no spots. It can be red with black flecks, black with yellow shoulder marks, chequered, netted, speckled or barred. When early naturalists put Linnaeus's binomial system into use, they went to town with ladybirds.

There was *sexmaculata* and *sexpunctata* for six-spotted ones; *octopunctata* had eight spots, *quadripunctata* four; *semicruciata* was halfway to having a cross on its back; *semifasciata* had half a stripe; *centromaculata* had spots down the middle; *triangularis* had three marks; *subpunctata* had small spots; *obscura* was obscurely marked. There was only one small problem – all these were the same species.

There are over 80 different named forms of the ten-spot ladybird, many once thought to be separate species, but now recognised as one species featuring different genetically controlled colour patterns. Geneticists are still trying to work out how these patterns are controlled at the level of the genes and the DNA.

These are not races or subspecies, where particular colour-ways occur in discrete geographical zones or different places around the world. The different patterns often occur together, and in breeding experiments many different patterns can appear in the offspring of identical 'normal' ten-spotted parents.

One selection pressure that can drive the evolution of a diversity of forms is the presence of predators that hunt by favouring one precise colour-way. Birds, in particular, hunt using a 'search-image' in their brains, seeing targets that match the image but missing others that look slightly different. By having many different patterns, at least some individuals should survive to reproduce. The only trouble with this theory in this case is that all ladybirds are brightly coloured to remind birds not to eat any of them because they taste horrid. Quite why the ten-spot ladybird should have such versatile patterns is still open to debate.

Most variable colour pattern

NAME **ten-spot ladybird** *Adalia decempunctata*

LOCATION Europe

ATTRIBUTE over 80 different named colour or pattern forms

Insects defend themselves from attack in many different ways. After hiding, possessing a weapon is one of the commonest strategies. The weapon may be biting or stinging an enemy, but it may also be simply tasting foul. Plenty of plants contain noxious chemicals to deter herbivores, and plant-feeding insects can take advantage of this fact by storing the poisons in their bodies.

There is one drawback for the individual with the poisonous body. Although birds (the main insect predators) may soon learn to avoid a particular species because it tastes disgusting, that is a bit late for the individual insect they have picked up, crushed, chewed and swallowed, even if they then vomit it back up again. It would be much better if the insect could warn off its potential predator by giving it a taste of what might come should the meal be fully consumed.

This is exactly what many beetles do. Rather than wait until their innards are squashed out in the bird's beak, they defensively squeeze out large droplets of their foul-tasting haemolymph (blood). As soon as the bird tastes the bitter chemicals, it spits out the not-so-tasty morsel more or less unharmed.

The commonest beetles to use this defence, called reflex bleeding, are ladybirds, which exude droplets of their yellow body fluids from special pores in their knee joints. The most spectacular, though, is the aptly named bloody-nosed beetle, *Timarcha tenebricosa*, which oozes out a great drop of bright-red liquor from its mouthparts.

Ladybirds are brightly coloured to emphasise the warning. *Timarcha* is a sombre black, but its colouring is equally obvious against the green of its meadow foodplants. This large, lumbering flightless leaf beetle has little to fear from predators and it feeds quite happily in broad daylight.

Bloodiest insect

NAME **bloody-nosed beetle** *Timarcha tenebricosa*
LOCATION Europe and Central Asia
ABILITY deliberately spits out its own blood

Most beautiful insect

NAME	**birdwing butterfly, in particular Wallace's golden birdwing**
	Ornithoptera croesus
LOCATION	Batchian (Bacan), Indonesia
ATTRIBUTE	beautiful enough to cause one of the world's most hardened travellers nearly to faint

Beauty is very much in the eye of the beholder; just look at some of the names cooked up by entomologists. Scientific names regularly include terms such as *formosa* (handsome), *splendidissima* (most splendid), *pulchrina* (beautiful), *nobilis* (noble), *venustus* (lovely) and *elegans* (elegant).

There are many insects worthy of the title 'most beautiful', but nowhere is this better described than in the words of Victorian naturalist, scientist and traveller Alfred Russel Wallace. In a time before research grants, Wallace financed his travels by making collections for wealthy patrons or selling the handsome and strange specimens when he returned home to Britain. The highest value specimens were fabulous birds of paradise and beautiful birdwing butterflies. He knew only too well the worth of his collections. On the morning of 6 August 1852, during his return across the Atlantic from South America, the ship on which he was travelling, the *Helen*, caught fire and sank. Wallace and the crew spent nine days in the open life boats before they were rescued, but all Wallace's specimens were lost.

Undeterred, he published his *Travels on the Amazon and Rio Negro* and was soon off exploring and collecting in Southeast Asia. He managed to bring his booty home safely this time, and captured the essence of exploration, discovery and the hunt for fantastical beasts in *Malay Archipelago*, published in 1859. On his first venture into the forests of Batchian (now Bacan), one of the Mollucan islands of Indonesia, he caught sight of a spectacular birdwing butterfly. It took him a further two months to finally collect a specimen. Wallace later named it *Ornithoptera croesus*, after the 6th-century BCE king of Lydia (now part of Turkey) famed for his wealth. Wallace's words still resonate today:

'The beauty and brilliancy of this insect are indescribable, and none but a naturalist can understand the intense excitement I experienced when I at length captured it. On taking it out of my net and opening the glorious wings, my heart began to beat violently, the blood rushed to my head, and I felt much more like fainting than I have done when in apprehension of immediate death. I had a headache the rest of the day, so great was the excitement produced by what will appear to most people a very inadequate cause.'

Longest head

NAME **giraffe-necked weevil** *Trachelophorus giraffa*
LOCATION Madagascar
ATTRIBUTE the longest head of any insect

It will come as no surprise to discover that some males have big heads. Big heads can be attached to big jaws (see page 60) or house big eyes (see page 56). But the male giraffe-necked weevil of Madagascar has the most awkward-looking head imaginable. And what does he use it for? Nodding.

The male's long, slender head takes up about 10 of his 25 mm (1 in) length. The neck is another 7 mm, making the insect's head and neck over 70 per cent of its entire body length. It holds them angled up from its squat body, like a miniature construction site crane. The female's head and neck are also relatively long, but only about half her total body length.

The male uses his stretched form for no practical purpose. The nodding, however, is very important to other giraffe-necked weevils. It seems that the males contest one another, trying to out-nod their opponents in ritualised fights. After head-to-head nodding competitions, one male will retreat. It also appears that the females choose the best nodders with which to mate. Thus, over evolutionary time, the males with the longest heads (better for nodding) have been selected.

The irony is that it is the female who really needs a long head. *Trachelophorus* belongs to a group of beetles called leaf-rolling weevils. She chews through both sides of a leaf blade to the mid-rib. The leaf now has a tendency to curl, a property that she harnesses using her angled neck and head to roll the partly severed plant into a small cigar. She lays an egg inside, and the grub is protected from predators and parasites while it feeds.

Most streamlined insect

NAME   **water pennies** in the family Psephenidae

LOCATION   worldwide

ATTRIBUTE   shaped to withstand rushing torrents

Despite rolling boulders and white water, life continues beneath the surface of fast-flowing rivers. There, attached to the stones in the water, live water pennies. So named because they are roughly the size of a one-cent coin (a penny), these creatures are the larvae of beetles. The adult beetles are terrestrial, but their larvae are wholly aquatic.

A water penny is multi-segmented, with each segment flattened into a flange that surrounds its body, hiding head, legs and gills beneath a smooth carapace. It clings tight to rocks and stones using its clawed feet. If it cannot get a purchase, then even slow-moving water can wash it away. The larvae spend most of the time under stones or pressed into small cracks in the rocks, feeding on microscopic algae. But they must leave the water to pupate, and at such times they are exposed to the force of the water.

In rapidly moving water, there is a boundary layer of calmer water at the bottom, slowed by friction with the river bed. Small and flattened, water pennies can sit within this layer, but they cannot afford to be complacent. As well as clinging on tight with their feet, they use hydrodynamics to hold fast. By pumping water out through the gaps between their segments and at the tail end of the body, they can reduce turbulence to creep slowly through the force of the flow.

Loudest insect

NAME   **dog day cicada** *Tibicen pronotalis*

LOCATION   North America

ABILITY   makes the loudest noise of any insect

Insects are generally small, secretive and quiet. Most are reluctant to draw attention to themselves, but the cicadas are an exception. Along with crickets, katydids and grasshoppers, the cicadas use sound to communicate with each other, and they do so in the loudest manner possible.

On each side of the first abdominal segment is a large round organ called the tymbal. The tymbal, just like a drum, has a stiff elastic membrane held taught by a rigid circular frame. Inside the insect's abdomen, a large muscle is attached by a narrow thread to the centre of the membrane. When the muscle contracts it distorts the tymbal membrane, causing it to buckle suddenly, creating an audible snap. When it relaxes, the membrane clicks back to its resting position. By vibrating the membrane at 4,000 to 7,000 times a second, the clicks become merged into a continuous whining buzz. Inside the abdomen, two air sacs (modified breathing tubes) are tuned to the natural frequency of the tymbals and act as amplifiers. The noise made is astounding, easily competing with loud power tools, lawn mowers or motorcycles. Cicadas on the motorway verge can often be heard from inside fast-moving cars, or through dense forest from over 1 km away.

The volume of a noise is measured using sound pressure level meters. The loudest sustained volume recorded for an insect is for an African cicada, *Brevisana brevis*, which clocked up 106.7 decibels. Human hearing is damaged by prolonged exposure to this volume and the recommended limit is less than two hours per day. *Brevisana* keeps it up all day long. The loudest peak cicada call ever recorded was for one of the North American dog day cicadas, *Tibicen pronotalis*, which reached 108.9 decibels during an alarm call. The normal purpose of cicada 'songs' is for males to call to females and announce territoriality to each other. On the whole the largest cicadas make the most noise, so everyone knows who is the biggest. Alarm calls are made as a defence against birds, and at these volumes the sound is truly repellent.

When, on 29 September 1907, the French aviation pioneer Louis Charles Breguet lifted off the ground in an erratic prototype helicopter, *Gyroplane 1*, he was trying to emulate a flight technique long mastered by insects – hovering. The ability to hang in mid-air, even for just a moment, is of paramount importance if an insect wants to land on a leaf or a flower, as there are no runways for a glide-down descent.

Because insects can flex (twist) their wings, thrust and lift can be generated by both backwards and forwards strokes. In the fastest insects, the power stroke (pushing backwards) and the recovery stroke (pulling the wings forwards again) generate nearly all thrust, with just enough lift to keep level flight. In hoverers, thrust and lift are directed straight down, with just enough power to support an insect stationary.

Among the best-known hovering insects are the hawkmoths and bee-flies, which hover apparently motionless while drinking nectar from a flower. Others include the hoverflies, named for their habit of hovering in a shaft of light, over a flower, or in a woodland clearing. That hovering is important to these large and brightly coloured insects is demonstrated by the fact that they have huge eyes; in the males there is very little else on the head except the eyes. The large eyes give all-round vision to monitor the air-space in every direction and to maintain a fixed hovering point in the air. The males have larger eyes as it is they that do most of the hovering, guarding a three-dimensional territory, seeing off other males and enticing females.

But even hoverflies are out-hovered by one other group of insects, which are rather small and drab. The obviously named big-headed flies have big heads and, again, the males are all eyes. Their vast eyes give the same clue to all-round vision and territoriality. But instead of hovering brazenly in the large air-space under the spreading bough of a tree, they choose a discrete bush or a small space within the herbage. To the entomologist they demonstrate their flying skills by hovering in the folds of the insect net or inside the small glass tube as they are examined under a hand lens.

Best hoverer

NAME	**big-headed flies** in the family Pipunculidae
LOCATION	worldwide
ATTRIBUTE	superb stock-still hovering

Ugliest insect

NAME   **lobster moth caterpillar** *Stauropus fagi*
LOCATION   Europe and northern Asia
ATTRIBUTE   the most plug-ugly bug

It is the strange and unorthodox that most greatly offends our senses. This, combined with a lack of knowledge, creates fear and misunderstanding. So it is with the caterpillar of the lobster moth. And although derided as a gothic monstrosity and grotesque beast by many writers, it is not to offend or frighten humans that this strange and unorthodox maggot has evolved. Birds trying to eat it are its greatest enemies, and it is from them it must hide, or defend itself.

Early natural philosophers recorded that this peculiar animal was half spider and half scorpion. With its crustacean-like form, it is easy to see how it gets its English name. Its swollen tail has long, thin appendages, threateningly sting-like in appearance. These are the 'anal claspers', which in most other caterpillars are the last pair of sucker feet on the end of the caterpillar's body. The second and third pair of front legs are also grossly lengthened and the caterpillar waves them about in an aggressive manner if disturbed.

Pretending to be dangerous is the last resort of the lobster moth caterpillar. It would rather remain motionless, undetected because it just does not look like an edible morsel. Its bizarre knobbly shape is likely to be overlooked by predators because instead of appearing like a 'normal' caterpillar (cylindrical, smooth, plump) it looks like a bit of shrivelled dead leaf.

The caterpillar does not always look so deformed. When it first emerges from its egg it resembles an ant, complete with long, skinny waist and round, bulbous abdomen. It can also exude formic acid, the same sharp-tasting chemical used by ants to dissuade birds from eating them. Incidentally, the word 'lobster', traced back through the Old English 'lopustre' and Anglo-Saxon 'loppestre' or 'lopystr', comes from a corruption of the Latin 'locusta' – perhaps an even uglier beast if its habits are taken into account.

The most obvious purpose of jaws is eating. But this is really a secondary use, because plenty of insects eat without the aid of jaws. There is an even more basic function – biting. An insect may bite to catch and kill prey, to manipulate soil or cut leaf particles, or to chew a burrow into wood. Each of these behaviours requires its own type of jaws. And the insect with the most remarkable jaws uses them for a most remarkable behaviour.

Grant's stag beetle, *Chiasognathus granti*, is sometimes also called Darwin's stag beetle because he pondered on it in his famous book *The Descent of Man*, but the insect had already been named in 1831 (the year Darwin set sail in HMS *Beagle*) after the Scottish naturalist Robert Grant. The beetle is found only in Chile and Argentina and is remarkable because a male's jaws can be as long as the rest of its body. However, unlike the powerful biting and cutting jaws of predatory or leaf-chewing insects, these mandibles are long and thin, and down-turned as they narrow to a fine point. They more resemble tweezers than secateurs – and this is exactly the use to which they are put.

Stag beetles are renowned for their antler-like jaws (see also page 242), which they use, not for biting and cutting, but for wrestling. *Chiasognathus* males joust for females (which only have normal, small mouthparts). They use their long jaws to try to pluck each other off branch perches near the rotten trees and logs in which the contested females will lay their eggs. The long, narrow jaws do not have the leverage to crush or bite each other. Darwin collected a specimen while travelling in South America and noted 'the mandibles were not strong enough to pinch my finger so as to cause actual pain'.

Chiasognathus males vary hugely in size, from 20 to 40 mm (0.8–1.6 in), with the jaws an extra 15 to 40 mm (0.6–1.6 in). The jaws are not always directly proportional to size, so some beetles are smaller than others, but longer-jawed. While feeding on low-nutrient rotten wood, the grub has several conflicting growth targets – to get as big as possible, to emerge and mate as soon as possible, and to grow the largest jaws. These conflicts create a wide variety of body sizes and jaw lengths, but the largest, best-nourished beetles, always have the longest jaws.

Largest jaws

NAME	**Grant's stag beetle** *Chiasognathus granti*
LOCATION	Chile and Argentina
ATTRIBUTE	jaws as long as the rest of its body

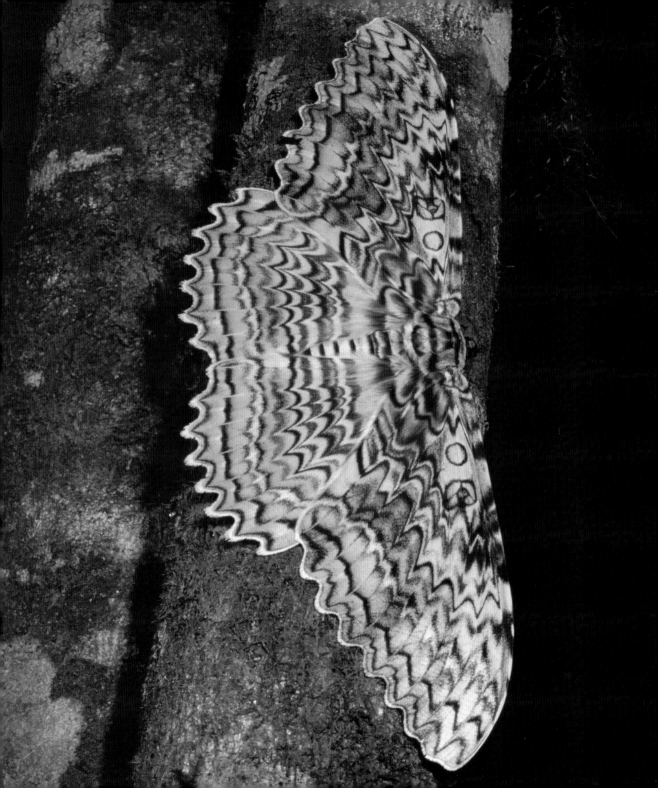

Largest wingspan

NAME	**ghost (or white witch) moth** *Thysania agrippina*
LOCATION	Central and South America
ATTRIBUTE	greatest wingspan of any living insect

It is generally held that large mammals occur in cooler regions, small mammals towards the equator. Conversely, small insects occur in temperate regions and large insects in the tropics. This rule is not hard and fast, but it is in the dark damp forests of the tropics that the insect world's giants are to be found. The tropics offer insects a stable environment denied them farther north or south. They are warm all year round: unlike in temperate lands there is no violent swing between the seasons, no winter cold through which the only survival is hibernation.

This constancy allows insect larvae to continue feeding and growing for much longer – usually all year round. The neotropics (Central and parts of South America) are not only home to the world's largest insect (see page 12), but also the insect with the greatest wingspan. The ghost moth, *Thysania agrippina*, can reach 305 mm (12 in) from wing tip to tip.

Surprisingly little is known about this magnificent giant. The caterpillar's food-plants are not recorded; mating, egg-laying and other life history behaviours are unknown. Despite its size, the moth is very well camouflaged against a tree trunk when it settles, wings fully outstretched and pressed down onto the similarly coloured and mottled bark.

Although the ghost moth has the greatest span, the Atlas moth, *Attacus atlas*, can reach 300 mm (11.8 in) and has the largest wings by area. Prehistoric insects of far greater size are known from fossils. Contenders for the greatest wingspan ever are *Meganeura monyi* and *Meganeuropsis permiana*, two huge dragonfly-like insects that flew over 250 million years ago. They had wingspans reaching 750 mm (nearly 30 in).

In a world dominated by the greens and browns of leaf, bark, stone and soil, it is not surprising that there are so many green and brown insects. Camouflage – hiding by merging into the background – is the most widespread form of body colouring. Every group of insects has species that are easy to overlook because they so closely resemble the lichen-covered bark, broken pebble or leaf vein on which they are resting.

Nowhere is this better illustrated than in the orange oakleaf butterfly, *Kallima inachus*. When resting, like most butterflies, *Kallima* holds its wings together up over its body, presenting only the undersides to view. The under surfaces are near perfect replicas of a dead leaf. The combination of mottled browns and beiges, pointed front and back wing tips linked by a broad, dark-shaded line, and irregular radiating narrow lines is completely convincing.

Every individual *Kallima* butterfly has its own unique pattern, ever so slightly different from every other individual. This only adds to the impression that it is just a piece of dead herbage. After all, no two dead leaves are exactly the same. On the other hand, the upper surface of every individual is the same – more or less all-over pale iridescent blue, front wings with dark tips and a bright diagonal flash of orange. The contrast between upper and lower wing patterns is a means of avoiding enemies. The flashing orange bars, so distinctive when the insect is on the wing, suddenly vanish when it settles, leaving any pursuing predator looking around for the wing flashes and unable to see the cryptic butterfly hidden among the brown and faded leaves.

There are two subtly different variants of this butterfly. The dry-season form is slightly larger and paler. The wet-season form is generally smaller and the camouflaged underside more richly and darkly coloured. This, perhaps, better mimics the darker appearance of dead leaves when they are damp.

Best camouflage

NAME	**orange oakleaf butterfly** *Kallima inachus*
LOCATION	northern India to China and Japan
ATTRIBUTE	perfectly mimicking a dead leaf

Most flying insects have transparent wings. The wings of flies, bees and wasps are typically clear membranes, although a few have dark, clouded or speckled wings. These are relatively small-winged insects, and they usually have large and brightly coloured bodies. Damselflies and dragonflies also have uncoloured wings, which are much larger and criss-crossed by a network of tiny interconnecting veins. This gives the impression of milky or clouded wings, or rainbow colours created by reflections from a thousand tiny mirrors. But by a strange irony, the most transparent wings are those of certain butterfies, usually renowned for their exceptional colours.

The glasswings are a rather mixed assortment of species. Some appear completely transparent; others have delicate shades; others have patches of colour; and others are fully coloured. This scattering of clear butterflies in different butterfly groups suggests that transparency has evolved separately several times. Glasswings are a notable feature of tropical Central and South America. In the gloom of the rainforests, the transparent wings of these butterflies make them almost invisible when they settle on leaf or flower.

A butterfly's gaudy colours come from the broad, flat pigmented scales that cover their wings. Glasswings are still covered with scales, but instead of a dense mosaic array of overlapping fan-shaped coloured tiles, they are reduced to a sparse dusting of tiny split hairs only visible under the microscope.

Glasswing butterflies are sometimes also called clearwings, but this name is more usually given to a group of moths with similarly transparent wings also lacking coloured scales. However, instead of making these day-flying moths look invisible, the narrow, clear wings emphasise the black-, yellow- or red-barred bodies, and help them look like bees and wasps.

Most transparent wings

NAME	**glasswing butterflies** various species
LOCATION	worldwide
ATTRIBUTE	almost perfectly transparent wings

Hairiest legs

NAME **female dance fly** *Rhamphomyia longicauda*
LOCATION eastern North America
ATTRIBUTE highly attractive shaggy legs

In a world where females are guaranteed maternity of their own offspring, males often have to compete with each other for access to mates, or put themselves on display so that a discerning female can choose. This selection pressure has given rise to ferocious male weapons (see page 60), strange male behaviour (see page 130) and bizarre male forms (see page 50). But the insect world is peculiar, and it is no surprise to discover that even this evolutionary rule can be broken. In the dance fly, *Rhamphomyia longicauda*, it is the females who display their alluring bodies to the choosy males.

Female dance flies do not hunt their own prey. Instead they rely on a male to bring them a protein-rich food gift (a dead insect) when they mate. In order to entice a male, they first have to convince one that they are a suitable receptacle for his sperm. Between 10 and 100 females gather together in a bobbing cloud just before sunset, and males arrive with their nuptial gifts. A male hovers below his chosen female, which drops down to make contact, and they fly off to mate on the wing.

The females of this species are renowned for their hairy legs. The middle and hind limbs are flattened and fringed along front and back edges with a long, thick comb of luxuriant hair. The females also have inflatable bags along each side of the abdomen, which they pump full of air when they are displaying. The males are attracted to the fattest females with the hairiest legs – in experiments they choose these features in models suspended from microfilament strands.

The rationale for this behaviour is as follows. By choosing the largest female, a male is also choosing the one that will lay the most, and best-nourished, eggs, the kind most likely to give rise to strong, healthy and large offspring. By using her inflatable body bags and dark hairy legs, a female creates the impression of being the largest without over-burdening herself. This is very important in a flying insect that needs to keep its weight down. Entomologists like to call this behaviour 'deception', but it may also be an 'honest' display because leg and body ornament size is just as likely to be a true indicator of a productive female as total body size.

Snappiest jaws

NAME   **trap-jaw ants** *Odontomachus bauri*

LOCATION   Central and South America

ATTRIBUTE   fastest predatory strike in the animal kingdom

Seemingly small insect jaws can possess a formidable muscular power. They can cut through the tough fibres of plant leaves or the hard timber of living and dead tree trunks. They can pick up many times the insect's own weight and carry it back to the nest or food store. But it is when used as weapons of attack and defence that jaws are at their most impressive. In certain large soldier ants and termites, where the head is little more than a housing for the jaws' massive muscles, considerable force can be brought to bear on prey or to repulse enemies. In an escalating arms race against prey, predators and each other, more and more dangerous weapons have evolved.

Soldiers of *Termes* and *Homallotermes* termites snap their jaws at prey, rather like humans might snap their fingers. By pressing the tips of the jaws together, huge tension is built up. The sudden sliding of one jaw past the other releases the tension in a burst of energy, and the jaw blades become two outward-flashing scimitars.

But even this is outdone by the trap-jaw ant, *Odontomachus bauri*, which snaps its jaws shut so quickly that it becomes airborne. Again, elastic muscular energy is stored by tensing the muscles, holding the jaws cocked against latches on the ant's upper lip. The latch release is so sudden and the jaw momentum so great that the insect is flung, spinning, into the air. As well as biting at a large enemy, the ant simultaneously retreats out of danger. It can also snap its jaws down onto the leaf or soil surface to ping away to safety.

Using high-speed video cameras, the speed at which the trap-jaw ant's jaws close has been measured at 35–64 metres/second (78–145 mph). The jaws take just 0.13 milliseconds (1/2300th of the blink of an eye) to shut, and generate 100,000 times the force of gravity (g force). This gives the insect the honour of having the fastest predatory strike in the animal kingdom.

Prettiest eyes

NAME   **horse flies** in the family Tabanidae

LOCATION   worldwide

ATTRIBUTE   striped, speckled, barred and
mottled eye patterns

Under high-power microscopy, insect eyes are revealed to contain a complex array of hexagonal lenses, each focusing light onto a column of light-sensitive cells inside. Outwardly the eyes appear as smooth domes or hemispheres, uniformly coloured, black, grey, brown or dark red. However, in some groups of flies these drab schemes are replaced by a bewildering series of brightly coloured patterns.

The horse flies (also called deer flies, forest flies, clegs or stouts) are blood-suckers and females need to take a blood protein meal from a mammal to mature their eggs. Their bodies are predominantly mottled greys and browns, perfect camouflage against a tree trunk. Their eyes, by contrast, are brightly patterned with stripes, bars or dots of red, blue and green, sometimes appearing metallic in the sunshine.

Each species has its own particular eye pattern, a useful tool for the entomologist trying to identify some of the 3,000 species known from around the world. The most likely purpose of these patterns is to improve colour vision. Light passing through differently coloured lenses on the eye is likely to give better contrast to the image formed in the insect's brain. This works a bit like the red and blue lenses of 3-D glasses used to watch movies.

The flies may need this extra visual acuity to help them find their food. Any added contrast will surely benefit an insect seeking 'prey' animals against a background that is almost totally green. Contrast is their chief means of location, and horse flies are particularly attracted to large dark shapes, including vehicles, garden sheds and washing on a line.

Most elegant eggs

NAME	**lacewings** *Chrysopa* and other species
LOCATION	worldwide
ATTRIBUTE	eggs laid individually on thin stalks

Egg-laying is a business that requires a great deal of care. For most species of insects the most important maternal decision (after selecting the best mate) will be where to lay the eggs. Since they cannot run away or fight back, eggs are a particularly vulnerable stage in the insect life cycle. They are also, well, egg-shaped, so trying to disguise them as something else is rather difficult too. Egg-laying strategies vary from careful positioning and clever hiding, to scattering so many that some are bound to get through the dangers.

Lacewings have evolved a peculiar and elegant egg-laying technique. Before the female lays each egg, she exudes a droplet of a silk-like secretion from the tip of her abdomen. Like spider and moth silk, the secretion is created liquid but immediately hardens into a tough, flexible solid as it is stretched and reacts with oxygen in the air. Using her long tail, the lacewing pulls the silk upwards, and it stiffens into a long, thin bristle. At the very top, and at the extreme of her tail's reach, she deposits a single egg, which is glued to the strand by the same silk material. Sometimes laid singly, most lacewing eggs are laid in clusters of 20 to 100 on leaves or stems, or under logs and stones.

Despite their small size, insect eggs are valuable food sources and it is thought that, raised up away from the surface in this way, the lacewing eggs are out of the reach of predators. Lacewing eggs are still attacked by microscopic egg parasitoids, however. These tiny 'wasps' fly down to land on the egg, laying their own minuscule egg inside, with the resulting grub eating the developing lacewing embryo.

The prime purpose of the egg stalk, in fact, appears to be to avoid being eaten by hungry brothers or sisters that have hatched first. When the voracious lacewing larva hatches, it can climb down its own stalk, but is less likely to climb its siblings'. It is easier for it to take its hollow, curved scimitar-like jaws off in search of aphids and other plant lice.

Largest eye markings

NAME   **owl butterflies** in the genus *Caligo*
LOCATION   South America
ATTRIBUTE   largest (and most realistic) eye markings

Large eyes are usually a sign that an animal is a predator. Most hunters use sight to size up and target their prey before pouncing and killing. The biggest and most dangerous hunters are birds and mammals, which is why they have such prominent and distinctive eyes – circular, domed and glossy. What better way to protect against attack than to possess large frightening eyes like these? This is a tactic adopted by many butterflies and moths.

The largest eye spots belong, not surprisingly, to large butterflies. The owl butterflies, *Caligo* species, of Central and South America take their name from the fact that the underside of each hind wing has a single huge round eye spot right in the middle. In museum specimens, with the wings set out flat and straight, the butterfly looks remarkably like a caricature of an owl. The eye markings are perfectly round, a white ring emphasises the large dark iris and pupil, and there is even a crescent of white, like a reflective glint, giving the impression of a moist, curved lens surface.

The only problem is that, in life, the butterflies never adopt such a wings-outstretched pose. Invariably, when the butterfly is resting on a twig or tree trunk, it folds its wings tight together upright over its back, presenting only one eye spot at a time towards any potential attacker. *Caligo* butterflies live in dense rainforest, and although they are well known in museum collections, little is known of their life history, ecology or behaviour. One theory suggests that the main predators of owl butterflies are *Anolis* lizards, hunting in the bushes and trees on which the butterflies are resting. These lizards establish territories, larger lizards (with larger eyes) seeing off smaller ones. Thus, if the settled *Caligo* butterfly resembles a large lizard head, a smaller lizard coming across it is likely to retreat rather than advance.

Lightest footstep

NAME   **water measurers** in the genus *Hydrometra*

LOCATION   ponds and streams worldwide

ABILITY   stalks on water

No matter how deep or shallow the water of a stream or lake, it is at the surface that much of the activity takes place. It is here that gas exchange takes place as oxygen is absorbed from the air, here that amphibious animals enter and leave the water, and here that drowning animals first make contact. The group of organisms found on the surface has its own name, the neuston.

Many neuston dwellers are agile hunters. They hunt by detecting vibrations (ripples) running across the surface, usually targetting small terrestrial invertebrates that have fallen into the water and are having difficulties.

Slowest and most secretive of these neuston insects are the water measurers (*Hydrometra*), sometimes also called marsh treaders. Like their speedy cousins, the water skaters, they have long, thin legs, covered at the tips with water-repellent hydrophobic hairs. These hairs rest on the meniscus of the surface tension and prevent the feet from becoming wetted. The body of the water measurer is slim and light and easily supported on the water. The head is almost comically long, with small but bulbous eyes perched on each side about halfway down. The long head has a deadly function – it houses beneath it the long stylet mouthparts with which it skewers its prey.

What *Hydrometra* lacks in speed it makes up for in quiet stealth. Feeling the water surface with its legs and long antennae, *Hydrometra* senses the vibrations made by floundering insects in the water around it, or water fleas (*Daphnia* species) just below the surface. Its usual prey are the small springtails, Collembola, which float in small rafts on the water surface, feeding on single-celled algae.

Furriest insect

NAME **bumblebees** in the genus *Bombus*

LOCATION Europe, Asia, North America and Andean South America

ATTRIBUTE densely covered with a layer of insulating hairs

Technically, insects do not have fur. Fur is the insulating hair layer of mammals. Nevertheless, many insects appear furry because they are covered all over with hairs, bristles or spines. The usual function of these hairs is defensive. Furry caterpillars, often called woolly bears, look soft and downy, but in reality they are tough and bristly. The stiff, brittle hairs break off in the mouths or beaks of would-be attackers and take on a needle-like quality, often reinforced by painful stinging venom inside the hollow shafts.

In bumblebees, however, the fluffy layer is truly analogous to fur, and has genuine insulating properties. This is ably demonstrated by the geographical spread of bumblebees, which are mainly cool temperate or mountain animals. A handful get into Southeast Asia, but in the tropics of Central and South America (the most richly diverse insect paradise on Earth) they are virtually absent. They are unknown in Africa, Arabia, India and Australia.

That bumblebees fare well in the cool is well known. They get out to forage at flowers earlier in the day, earlier in the year, farther north and farther up mountains than other insects.

They achieve this by regulating their body temperatures better than most insects. To achieve flight, insects need to warm up. Most are unable to do this without help, and need to bask in the early-morning sun until a critical heat threshold is reached. Bumblebees can warm themselves up by shivering: they uncouple their wings then vigorously vibrate the large flight muscles in the thorax to generate metabolic heat, just as birds and mammals do when they are active. Once airborne, their thick coating of fur helps to insulate them against the cold.

Bee hairs are not simple narrow strands. Under a microscope they are revealed to be feathery plumes, each stalk branched all along its length. This is thought to have evolved partly to aid the collection of pollen grains, which get trapped in the branches. The divided hairs also better trap an insulating layer of warm air against the bee's body.

Ironically, bumblebees are at considerable risk of overheating. To cool down, they divert the flow of internal body fluids past a bare (and therefore not insulated) patch of cuticle on the underside of the abdomen – a heat window.

Most poisonous insect

NAME **African arrow-poison beetles** in the genera *Diamphidia* and *Polyclada*

LOCATION Botswana and Namibia

ATTRIBUTE used by bushman hunters to poison their arrows

Poisons are usually discovered after the accidental eating of them. The powerful poisons ricin (from castor beans), belladonna (from deadly nightshade fruits) and digitalis (from foxglove leaves) were all discovered after humans or their animals ate them.

Insects are not a large part of the human diet, so there are few opportunities for any toxic chemicals they contain to show their effects. There is, however, a group of insects that are deliberately exploited by humans for their deadly poisonous nature.

The bushmen of the northern Kalahari dig up leaf beetle pupae (*Diamphidia* and *Polyclada* species) from the soil under their shrubby foodplants. They then squeeze out the haemolymph (insect blood) from about ten pupae onto the shaft of an arrow (not the point in case they accidentally scratch themselves). The poison, known as diamphotoxin, is still not fully identified, but seems to be a long-chain polypeptide protein. In laboratory tests it has been found to be highly toxic to mice. It appears to work by breaking down the red blood cells, causing the collapse of the circulatory system then death. The much larger targets of the hunters take hours to die – days for a giraffe – and have to be tracked until they collapse.

The pupae of each species of leaf beetle are attacked by the larvae of a specialist predatory ground beetle (*Lebistina* species). There are no scientific measures of these predatory beetles, but the Kalahari bushmen value squeezed *Lebistina* larvae above the *Diamphidia* or *Polyclada*.

Diamphotoxin is poisonous to mammals only if it enters the blood stream; it is harmless if eaten. This begs the as yet unanswered question, why the beetles are so toxic if they gain no protection from predatory mice, rats and other insectivores eating them? Dried and smoked with tobacco, the beetle pupae induce drunkenness and hallucinations in the bushmen.

Most heavily armoured insect

NAME **rubytail wasps** in the family Chrysididae
LOCATION worldwide
ATTRIBUTE the toughest hide to protect them from stings and bites

Insects, along with all other arthropods (the jointed-limbed animals, including spiders, scorpions, crabs, lobsters and woodlice), have a tough exoskeleton on the outside, which protects the soft, vulnerable musculature on the inside. Strong and light, the exoskeleton is also waterproof, flexible and can be shaped into almost any structure. At its lightest it forms the diaphanous transparent wings of bees and flies. At its hardest, the outer covering, or cuticle, covers huge beetles in crush-proof armour.

The main strengthening and weight-supporting substance in insect cuticle is chitin. A chitin molecule is a polymer, in which smaller molecular units are joined end-to-end to make very long chains. The chains are aligned into sheets, which are multi-layered like plywood. The thickness of the chitin varies from species to species. Large beetles have very thick skins, but relative to their size the most heavily armoured insects are small. Rubytail wasps rarely reach more than 15 mm (½ in), but under a lens they are revealed to be awesome corrugated beauties. Their extra-thick cuticles are densely sculpted with ridges, mounds, pits and crevices.

Rubytails are cleptoparasitoids. They lay their eggs in the nests of bees or wasps. When the eggs hatch, the rubytail grubs eat the host brood and the foodstores laid in for them (earning them their other name – cuckoo wasps). The rubytail's lifestyle is difficult and dangerous, since their large hosts are armed with powerful jaws and deadly stings. Their defence against discovery in the nest is to have skin too thick for their hosts to puncture either by jaw or stinger. They do not have stings themselves. Instead they fold their head, thorax and short, stout abdomen into a tight curl, pull in legs and antennae, and rely on their armour. It has been known for a frustrated host to pick up a folded rubytail in its jaws and forcibly eject it through the nest entrance.

Longest wing tails

NAME **moon moths** in the genus *Actias*

LOCATION East Asia

ATTRIBUTE long hind wing tails

The main purpose of insect wings is to carry their owners in flight. For millions of years, before the appearance of birds or bats, insects were the only creatures able to fly, and this enabled them to colonise almost the entire Earth.

Having wings comes with a cost as well as a benefit. Wings have to be grown at the end of the larval stage, so extra nutrients are needed. They have to be expanded with air on emergence from the chrysalis, a process during which the soft insect is vulnerable. They have to be camouflaged to avoid attention, or coloured as a warning that their owner is poisonous. This has led to the evolution of strange patterns and shapes.

The moon moths are among the world's most impressive and attractive insects. They are large, subtly yet beautifully coloured, and striking in their shape and form. Perhaps their most noticeable feature is the long tails that stretch out from the hind wings. These vary from species to species, but are usually longer in the males, and can be over 100 mm (4 in) long in a moth with a similar wingspan.

Despite their strangely encumbered wings, the males are strong and swift fliers, moving easily and readily in search of females, which signal their presence by the release of sex pheromones (chemical scents). The purpose of the tails is not completely known, but the usual suggestion is that the moths gain protection from them.

The argument goes like this. In flight the streaming tails, often twisted near the tip, catch the eye of a predator (usually a bird) and act like an alternative target for the attack. If the tip of the tail is pecked off, the moth continues on its way. The bird is left with a beakful of rather tasteless scales and dry wing membrane. Occasionally wing-bitten moths are found and the peck marks to their tails are put forward as supporting evidence for this idea.

Best burrower

NAME	**mole crickets** in the genus *Gryllotalpa*
LOCATION	worldwide
ATTRIBUTE	mole-like burrowing habits

Animals that are adapted for burrowing, known as fossorial, are usually narrow, often squat and more or less cylindrical, and have short, powerful spade-shaped legs for shovelling soil. Burrowing insects include soil-nesting bees and wasps, dung beetles and cicada nymphs.

It is for their similarity to the burrowing mammal that mole crickets are named. They are large insects, with body lengths up to 50 mm (2 in) and a diameter of about 10 mm (½ in). They have small antennae, short wings and stout legs. The front legs are powerful spades, flattened for shovelling and with rugged spines to dislodge soil particles. They live in the soil of meadow, prairie and savannah lands, and relic populations sometimes occur in gardens and parks. Loss of habitat is restricting many species across the world.

The presence of mole crickets in the landscape is revealed to us, not by their burrows, which are often concealed and difficult to spot, but by their pleasant and distinctive churring songs. Like most crickets, they 'sing' by rubbing their wings together. A plectrum on the upper side of the left wing scrapes a row of pegs on the underside of the right wing, causing a rasp. This is amplified by parts of the wing membranes, and also by the trumpet shape of the burrow, inside the entrance of which the male sits while he calls.

The mole crickets' wings are not just for singing – they regularly come to the surface and can fly. Although clumsy and apparently directionless, these stubby and ungainly insects take to the air on warm summer evenings.

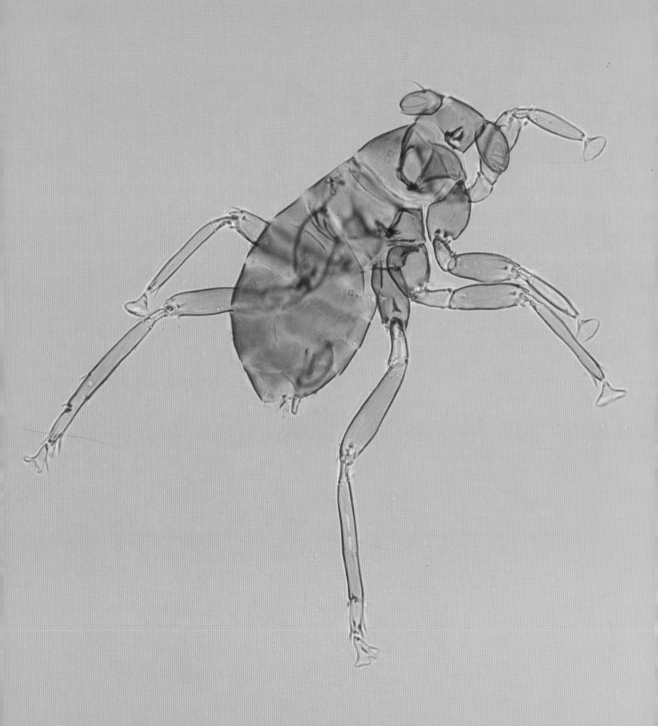

Smallest insect

NAME   **fairy fly** *Dicopomorpha echmepterygis*
LOCATION   USA
ATTRIBUTE   smallest adult insect

Insects are small. Even the largest, most heavily built insects are relatively small compared to vertebrates. For every very large insect in the world, there are countless numbers of very tiny species. All insects start out small, as an egg, but for the sake of sensible comparison, it is the adult stage – after emergence from the pupa (chrysalis) or final moult – that needs to be considered. The search for the smallest insect starts with the knowledge that insect growth occurs only during the larval period, as caterpillar, maggot, grub or nymph. Since low nutritional input usually means small adult size, where better to look for the tiniest insect than actually inside the small nutritional packages that are the eggs of other insects?

The Mymaridae, called fairy flies for their minute and delicate forms under the microscope, are distantly related to bees and wasps. Long known for their small size, they are egg parasitoids, laying their eggs inside the eggs of other insects. A parasitoid devours its host organism from within, eventually killing it. It is, in effect, an internal predator. The fairy fly grub eats the host embryo and yolk food store before making its own cocoon, changing into a pupa, and emerging as an adult. Its entire feeding life is spent inside a single insect egg, so even the largest fairy flies are very small indeed.

The smallest mymarid known is the male of *Dicopomorpha echmepterygis*, discovered in Illinois in 1997. The smallest adult male recorded is 139 μm (0.139 mm, or about 1/200 inch) long. Many protozoa (single-celled animals) are larger than this.

Dicopomorpha echmepterygis breeds in the eggs of a bark louse, *Echmepteryx hageni*, itself a tiny insect. Usually each *Echmepteryx* egg contains one to three males and a female *Dicopomorpha*. The males are blind and wingless and never leave the host egg. Instead they use their long legs to grapple the larger (nearly 200 μm, 0.2 mm or about 1/125 inch) female during mating. She will finally emerge to fly off and parasitise further bark-louse eggs.

Heaviest insect

NAME   **giant weta** *Deinacrida heteracantha*

LOCATION   Little Barrier Island, New Zealand

ATTRIBUTE   heaviest recorded living insect

Most of what we know about insects was learned through specimens collected for museums and private collectors. Museum specimens are fixed and tangible items and (so long as they have data labels) they are attached to precise details of where and when they were found. Insect specimens are easy to preserve. They just need to dry out and they will last for centuries. The one important thing they lose is water, and with this loss also comes great loss of weight. So when a measure of body mass is required, museum specimens are of limited use. Animals must be weighed alive.

Accurate weight records for insects are sparse. There is, however, a good chance that a giant weta, *Deinacrida heteracantha*, from Little Barrier Island, off the northeast coast of New Zealand's North Island, is the world's heaviest insect.

Despite giant proportions, the large beetles so distinctive of the tropics (see page 12) are relatively light – after all, they are good flyers. Wetas on the other hand are earthbound. Isolated in New Zealand for 80 or so million years without mammalian predators, they evolved flightlessness and huge size. When rats and cats arrived with humans, many wetas became endangered and conservation plans were formulated to save them. Like newborn babies, they have been coddled and carefully weighed.

A heavily gravid (bloated with eggs) female specimen has been accurately measured at 71 g (about 2½ oz). For an insect 80 mm (3 in) long, this is a true heavyweight. To put it into perspective, most 80 mm beetles probably weigh 5 g, and 80 mm birds (excluding any long tail) about 12 g. No wonder wetas don't fly.

Fastest flier

NAME   **hawkmoths (sphinx moths, hornworms)**
in the family Sphingidae
LOCATION   worldwide
ATTRIBUTE   fastest sustained flight (probably)

In 1926, in a laughable example of miscalculation, an entomologist reported that a deer bot fly, *Cephenomyia pratti*, streaked past so fast that he estimated it was travelling at 400 yards (370 m) per second. Deer bots chase deer to lay their eggs in their nostrils; the maggots then chew into the nasal flesh. Needless to say the deer don't like it and try to run away. The flies give chase and certainly achieve high speeds, but not the 1300 km/h (818 mph) reported. That would mean the insect breaking the sound barrier.

One of the problems with estimating flight speed is that part of the movement comes from the speed of the wind carrying the insect along. Monarch butterflies are recorded keeping up with cars travelling at 40 km/h (25 mph) and dragonflies with light aircraft travelling at 145 km/h (90 mph), but these reports tell us nothing about these insects' true flying speed.

Experiments with caged or tethered insects in wind tunnels are woefully thin on the ground. The 'official' fastest insects so far recorded are locusts, measured at 33 km/h (21 mph), but this is only because they have actually been measured and other less troublesome insects have not.

A group of Boston entomologists chose to look at one of the obvious contenders: a hawkmoth, also called a sphinx moth (after the stout caterpillar's rearing defence pose) or hornworm (after the thorn on the caterpillar's tail). These aerodynamic insects are well known for their flying prowess, and several species are long-distance migrants. It is a shame that the species chosen to be measured was a rather tubby agricultural pest – the tobacco hornworm, *Manduca sexta* – rather than one of its slimmer and racier cousins. The entomologists calculated that the moth may be able to fly at 36 km/h (22.5 mph). Others will certainly fly faster, if they are ever measured.

Fastest runner

NAME	**tiger beetles** particularly *Rivacicindela* species
LOCATION	Australia
ATTRIBUTE	insect land speed record-holder at 9 km/h (5.6 mph)

Tiger beetles are so called because of their fierce hunting abilities. They have large, powerful, curved jaws to crush their insect prey and long legs to run it down. Most species can fly, but do so only to escape their enemies, taking airborne hops for 10-20 metres (30-60 feet) before landing again and disappearing into the undergrowth.

Like other fast, terrestrial insects, tiger beetles run using an alternating tripod, with three of their six legs pushing against the ground at any one time (front and back legs on one side, middle leg on the other) while the other three legs move forwards through the air ready for the next push.

Tiger beetles are found all over the world and their fast running-speed is well known, but when accurate measurements were made of one small group of species in the subgenus *Rivacicindela*, in Australia, the results were astonishing. Not only were they fast, they were the fastest insects ever measured. Clocking up an average of 1.8 metres/second (6.5 km/h, 4 mph) and a maximum of 2.5 m/s (9 km/h, 5.6 mph), *Rivacicindela hudsoni* (the largest species at 20 mm (⅘ in) long) easily beat the record of the insect previously believed to be the fastest – the cockroach *Periplaneta americana*, maximum speed 1.5 m/s (5.4 km/h, 3.4 mph).

Unlike many other tiger beetles across the world, *Rivacicindela* species are wingless and cannot fly. They may have evolved their rapid gait to compensate for this loss of flight when fleeing predators. The typical escape strategy is a series of wild zigzags followed by a straight, bullet-like exit.

Flightlessness often evolves in island-dwelling insects, where flying is a liability, since there is the danger of taking off and being blown out to sea. The *Rivacicindela* beetles occur only in the narrow bands of sand dune and scrub around the dry salt lakes of South and Western Australia. Here, any insect taking to the wing is in danger of being blown onto the inhospitable salt pan of the lake or away into the arid desert that surrounds it.

Longest tongue

NAME **Morgan's sphinx** *Xanthopan morganii*
LOCATION Central Africa and Madagascar
ATTRIBUTE tongue up to 35 cm (13.8 in) long

One of Charles Darwin's lesser-known, but still impressively erudite, books was *On the various contrivances by which British and foreign orchids are fertilised by insects*, published in 1862. In it he recounts how he became fascinated by some Madagascan orchids, *Angraecum sesquipedale*, that he had been sent.

The scientific name '*sesquipedale*' means 'foot-and-a-half long' and refers to the thin, whip-like hollow spur running backwards 35 cm (just over a foot) from the inside of the flower. This is no mere decorative tweak: it is one of the most important parts of the bloom because at the end of the tube is the nectary. Darwin surmised that the plant must be visited by moths with tongues capable of reaching down into the nectar.

His proposal was confirmed in 1903, when a subspecies of an African hawkmoth with a 30-cm (12-in) proboscis was found on the island. It was named, in honour of Darwin's prediction, *Xanthopan morganii praedicta*. There is now some debate whether this subspecies is different from mainland specimens – although the moth was first described in 1856, its tongue length was not fully appreciated for nearly 50 years.

The flying moth finds the blooms at night by their scent, hovering close by to test the air-borne chemicals with its antennae. Then it backs up, extends its tightly coiled proboscis and slides it deep into the corolla tube, down to the nectar at the bottom.

This bizarre example of parallel evolution in flower and tongue length beautifully illustrates how extreme structures in both plants and animals can occur. It might at first seem a paradox that the flower should develop longer and longer flowers, for this would surely make it increasingly difficult for insects to visit and so decrease the chances of successful pollination. Likewise the moth's investment in a long tongue would not be necessary if it visited the plentiful supply of shorter flowers available.

But both moth and plant win out by this mutual evolution. The moth's gain is exclusive access to the *Angraecum* nectar – no other insect has a tongue long enough to compete with it. The orchid's benefit is an exclusive pollinator, which visits only one plant species so does not waste precious pollen by smearing it onto other flower species.

Smelliest insect

NAME	**goat moth** *Cossus cossus*
LOCATION	Europe and Asia
ATTRIBUTE	caterpillar smells of male goats

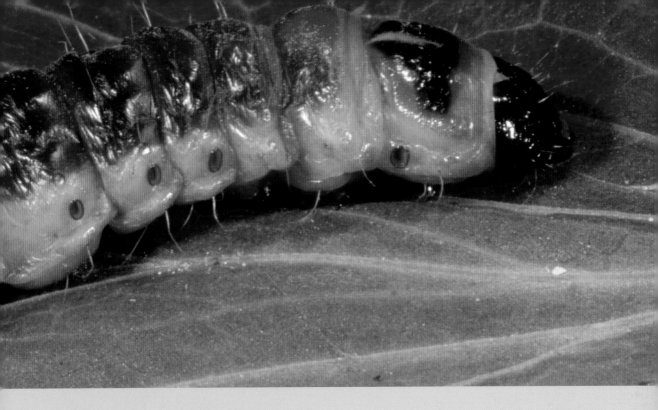

Insects use smell to navigate the world. They follow the scent of flowers after nectar and pollen. They smell out the leaves of the right food-plants on which to lay their eggs and which their caterpillars will eat. And they follow the wind-carried trail of sex pheromones to find each other. Insect smelling organs are located on the antennae, variously shaped spines, cups and pits with minute holes to let in the airborne chemicals they seek. So sensitive are these receptors that some will react to just a single molecule of the sex scents, given out usually by females trying to attract males.

What then of the many insects commonly called 'stink' bugs? They are the shieldbugs and close relatives the leaf bugs. These large, stout insects suck plant sap, and many are brightly coloured to warn potential predators that they taste foul. If picked up in beak, claw or entomologist's fingers they leak out an oily liquid from glands on the thorax. Eye-wateringly bitter to the taste, the chemicals contain cyanide compounds.

The strongest insect smell comes from the caterpillar of the goat moth, *Cossus cossus*. This large, tubby grey moth gets its name not from any goat markings on its wings or association with living goats, but because its pink fleshy caterpillars smell like billy goats. The large, smooth larvae spend three or four years boring into the living timber of willows, poplars, oaks and other trees. Large colonies sometimes occur, causing considerable damage to individual trees, which weep sap and fluid decay from the deep burrows.

The smell of goat is strong enough (and unpleasant enough) to be detected some distance downwind, and many other insects, including beetles and flies, are attracted to lay their eggs in the damaged, diseased and rotting wood that results from the caterpillars' burrowing. Exactly what purpose the goat scent serves is unclear. It may act like a pheromone, alerting other goat moths to lay their eggs, thus ensuring some cross-breeding in the future genetic stock.

Most subterranean insect

NAME   **Cooloola monsters** in the genus *Cooloola*

LOCATION   Queensland

ATTRIBUTE   live their entire lives underground

Insects are the only invertebrates with wings. Flight has given them the ability to spread throughout the world, colonise habitats from the open ocean to the tops of mountains, locate sparsely spread food (and mates), catch each other to eat, and avoid some larger predators. Having wings is one of the basic attributes of being an insect, so not having them is something of a novelty.

A few well-known groups of insects (fleas and lice, for example) have, over evolutionary time, lost their wings, which would just get in the way of their normal life burrowing into their hosts' hair and feathers. So too, insects do not need wings if they spend all their lives burrowing in the soil. The most subterranean of all live in Australia.

In 1980, entomologist D.C.F. Rentz found a bizarre humpbacked creature, rather resembling a large cicada nymph, burrowing in the sandy soil of the Cooloola National Park in Queensland. It defied immediate classification, other than that it was a distant relative of grasshoppers and crickets. It now luxuriates in the wonderful name of Cooloola monster, *Cooloola propator*, in the new family Cooloolidae.

Since that initial discovery, three more *Cooloola* species have been found in and around the same area of Queensland. Very little is known about their biology or life histories. There are no other known relatives with which to make comparisons, so the only information available is from a handful of specimens kept under laboratory conditions. Two facts emerge: the Cooloola monsters live all their lives underground; and they probably eat other soil-dwelling invertebrates. There is still a lot of research to be done.

Fastest wing-beat

NAME   **biting midges** in the genus *Forcipomyia*
LOCATION   North America, Europe, Asia
ATTRIBUTE   fastest wing-beat of any creature

True flight, using muscle-powered wings, has evolved four times: in birds, mammals (bats), reptiles (extinct pterosaurs) and insects. In the first three, which are vertebrates, the wings are (or were) powered by direct attachment of large flight muscles, which pull the wings up and down, contracted by stimulation of nerve cells. In these large animals this is a perfectly acceptable mechanism, since they require only large, slow stokes of the wing (sunbirds and hummingbirds get to only 90 strokes/second). This allows sufficient time, not for the muscles to recover, but for the nerves to reset, ready to be fired again.

Some large and 'primitive' insects, like dragonflies, also use direct flight muscles to power large, slow wing-beats that reach 100 strokes/second. But flies, bees, wasps, butterflies, beetles – indeed, most 'modern' insects – use another method of wing power, with indirect muscle attachment. Their flight muscles are not attached to the wings, but are fixed to the inside of the thorax near the wing bases. When they contract, they distort the flexible thoracic box, levering the wings upward; when they relax, the box snaps back to its former shape and the wings are pulled down. The muscles are not triggered by direct nerve impulse. Instead, as the thorax passes back through the snap point, the sudden movement stimulates the next muscular contraction to occur. The nerves only fire occasionally to keep the beats regular, or to start flying from a standstill.

Small, light insects have the fastest wing-beats, and of these flies are the fastest of all since they have only two wings to control, while other insects have four. The fastest wing-beats recorded are in tiny biting midges from the genus *Forcipomyia*, whose wings beat at a minimum of 1,046 strokes/second.

Smallest egg

NAME **parasitoid flies** in the family Tachnidae

LOCATION different species worldwide

ATTRIBUTE smallest recorded insect egg

The creation and survival of the next generation is, after surviving the dangers of this generation, the prime directive of living organisms. It begins with the fertilisation of an egg by a sperm. What happens to the egg next depends very much on the lifestyle of each species. At one extreme, typical of mammals, individual eggs are nurtured as embryos inside the mother's body until they are mature enough to withstand the rigours of the outside world. At the other extreme, eggs are spread here, there and everywhere in the expectation that at least some of them will get through to adulthood. There is a trade-off. Low numbers of large eggs can provide a good nutritional start, but they are the target of specialist predators and parasitoids and can be difficult to hide. Small eggs do not provide much in the way of initial nourishment, but they can be generated in prodigious numbers so that some are guaranteed to escape detection or being eaten.

In a twist of evolutionary history, the smallest known insect eggs are small so that they will get eaten. The smallest recorded insect eggs belong to a fly, *Clemelis pullata*, which lays many thousands of 'microtype' eggs, only 27 μm long (0.027 mm, 1/1000 inch). These are scattered over leaves in the hope that they will be eaten by moth caterpillars. The eggs are so small that they are swallowed whole. Once inside the caterpillar's digestive tract, the eggs hatch and the resulting maggots eat their victim alive, from within.

Clemelis eggs are smaller than the eggs of the smallest known insect, *Dicopomorpha echmepterygis* (see page 90). *Dicopomorpha* eggs are laid within the eggs of other insects, but are larger than *Clemelis* eggs as they are targeted and laid in low numbers (three or four per host egg). Measuring insect eggs is not a widespread activity amongst entomologists. It is no surprise, therefore, that accurate measurements are few. *Clemelis* eggs are important because the fly is known to parasitise (among others) coddling moth, a serious orchard pest of apples and pears. It is likely that other parasitoids will have eggs of similar size or smaller, but nobody has ever looked for them.

The best place to lay an egg is in a nest. Only a few insects make nests, however. Most lay their eggs on a leaf, under a stone, or on a log, and then walk away. Nests offer safety, warm (or cool) dry conditions, and shelter from any number of predators and enemies. Not all nests work in the same way – there are a number of different arrangements for bringing on the next generation.

The honeybees, ants and termites are generally considered the most advanced and evolved of all insect societies. They live in groups numbering thousands or even millions, have different castes, division of labour, tactile and chemical communication and long-lived egg-laying queens, and their colonies can be virtually immortal.

The evolutionary route of these truly social colonies is not completely known, but it can be guessed by looking at some of the other nest forms taken by their relatives. Most bees and wasps make nests, and provision them with food for the grubs that hatch from eggs laid, usually singly, in small separate cells.

In most species, a mother dies before the larvae reach maturity and she never sees her offspring. But in a few, the daughters cohabit with their slightly longer-lived mother, and help to expand the nest burrow to create more cells for grandchildren and beyond.

The carpenter bees, *Xylocopa* species, are large, robust insects, and get their name from their habit of chewing nest burrows into tree trunks, logs and other dead timber. These bees have started on the road towards sociality, and two generations commonly live together in their chewed wooden nests.

In low numbers, ranging from half-a-dozen to twenty or so, such sub-social bees cannot offer their young the support of separate nurse, guard, forager and cleaner bees to look after them. But they do give their offspring a good nutritional start to their larvahood by laying the largest eggs of any insect. One species, *Xylocopa auripennis*, is moderately large at nearly 40 mm (1½ in) long, but it lays relatively giant eggs 16.5 mm by 3 mm (⅔ by ⅛ inch).

Largest egg

NAME **carpenter bees** in the genus *Xylocopa*
LOCATION worldwide
ATTRIBUTE lay the largest eggs

Spikiest insect

NAME   **hedgehog leaf beetles** in the genera *Hispa* and *Hispella*

LOCATION   northern hemisphere

ATTRIBUTE   covered all over with spines

Spines are a good deterrent against predators. In the mammalian world they are found in hedgehogs, porcupines and echidnas (spiny ant-eaters), while among reptiles there are thorny devils. In the insects, spines are everywhere. There are bristly flies, hairy caterpillars, spiny bush-crickets and horned beetles. With so many examples of sharp, prominent spikes, all with different origins, choosing the spikiest has been a hard task.

Hairy or prickly caterpillars are covered all over with long spines. Quite where a hair becomes a prickle is open to debate. Whether they are soft to the human touch or rough, they all have the same effect in the gullet of a predator, where they break off and stick in the delicate skin of mouth, beak or throat. In some species, the hairs are hollow and laced with stinging venom.

Lone spines or horns normally serve to demonstrate the size (and therefore prowess) of their owners – usually males – to females. Beetles that breed in rotten timber or dung are often armed with enormous horns on the head or thorax or both, but they are usually single or paired, and the rest of the body is unadorned. Bugs and bush-crickets are often armed with stout thorns on the head, thorax and sometimes the legs. These probably serve to prevent their being eaten. In a few leaf-hopper bugs and some beetles, the whole body is shaped like one enormous horn – an animated thorn. This disguises them on the stems of their food-plants among genuine thorns. But, again, this is just one horn.

After much consideration, the prize for the spikiest insect goes to a group of hedgehog-like leaf beetles, *Hispa*, *Hispella* and other closely related species. Although these are only a few millimetres long, they are covered across their entire carapace with long, powerful spines. These are not just stout hairs, but genuine horns rising out of the insect's cuticle. In some species the legs and antennal segments are also armed. The prickles' purpose is still a mystery.

Biggest feet

NAME **water, or diving, beetles** in the family Dytiscidae

LOCATION worldwide

ATTRIBUTE males have hugely broadened and flattened front feet

Feet have two purposes: for walking and for holding on. The insect foot, strictly called the tarsus (plural tarsi), is made up of one to five segments, and usually ends in a pair of claws. In its simplest form, for example in cockroaches or ground beetles, which run across the ground, the segments are small and narrow and strung together like the beads of a necklace. Insects that have to climb plants, rocks or timber often have greatly enlarged claws, like grappling hooks.

The biggest feet of all are for gripping smooth surfaces, and the most important smooth surface is the back of the female during mating. Female leaf beetles are smooth and shiny, and the males have large feet, but the slipperiest females are streamlined water beetles. It is no surprise, then, that the largest, flattest feet, belong to male water beetles.

In the males of the freshwater diving beetles in the family *Dytiscidae*, the first three segments of the front tarsus are grossly dilated and flattened into a round pad. This tarsal pad is fringed around its edge with a skirt of short, stout hooked hairs, and underneath it is covered all over with a series of large and small sucker cups.

The females' feet are narrow and dainty, but their backs are often hairy or sculpted with broad grooves, dimples and lumps. It was originally thought that these rough areas 'helped' the males by giving them a textured surface on which to grip. But in fact sucker cups need to form a tight seal to hold, and this is broken by a wrinkled texture. It now appears that the puckered carapace of the female water beetle is there to help her throw off her suitors, at least until she is ready to mate.

Largest claws

NAME **giant mantid** *Macromantis hyalina*
LOCATION Central and South America
ATTRIBUTE largest claws in the insect kingdom

Claws are for holding on: to the ground, to rocks, to plants, to each other or to prey. Over evolutionary time, insect claws have adapted to fit precisely around whatever it is that they are used for grasping. Most insect legs end with one or two curved, hook-like structures used for clinging on to the leaves or tree trunks up which they crawl. Large, heavy tree-dwelling insects have more substantial grappling irons to prevent their falling; light runners have delicate crochet hooks that give purchase but do not get in the way.

The largest claws, though, are for clinging on to things that struggle to escape. Lice have huge muscular hands with a moveable finger claw that grips individual hairs on their host. A louse can move around securely, but is difficult to dislodge by grooming. Similarly, fleas have stout crook-shaped claws. However, in a parallel to birds and mammals, the largest claws are those used to bring down prey, and the most awesome claws are possessed by the most impressive of hunters – the mantids.

Mantids can appear slight and feeble, with their narrow bodies, delicate triangular heads and long, flimsy legs, but they have a power to overcome creatures far more muscular than themselves. They rely on the same sudden killing mechanism used by birds of prey: owls, eagles, falcons and hawks. These fearsome birds kill, not with their beaks, but with their claws – their sharp, curved, powerful talons.

The front legs of mantids are developed into large, curved and spined gripping and killing weapons. The articulated claw is made from the third and fourth leg sections, the femur and tibia – analogous to thigh and calf of larger animals. The combination of lethal shape and ferocious speed allows mantids to attack and devour quite surprising prey. They can snatch a dragonfly out of mid-air, crush large armoured beetles and disable stinging bees and wasps in the blink of an eye. They are not above attacking vertebrate prey either – small frogs, lizards and even mice are all eaten.

The longest mantid is the African *Ischnomantis gigas*, with females up to 17 cm (7 in), but these are very slender creatures with weedy limbs. The largest claws belong to the tropical American *Macromantis hyalina*, which is altogether a much stouter and more impressive beast.

Extreme

Evolution

Most punctual insect · Giddiest insect · Most useful young · Best mutual coexistence · Largest overwintering congregation · Largest colony · Most generous nuptial gift · Best passenger · Most necrophilic insect · Cleverest digger · Most violent sex act · Biggest plant distortion · Best thermometer · Best architect · Cleverest drinker · Most dangerous egg-laying strategy · Most adventurous insect · Most disgusting habits · Most cold-tolerant insect · Most devious prey trap · Most untrusting sex act · Best sculptor · Most unusual foodstuff · Most extreme metamorphosis · Best eyesight · Best mimic · Biggest migration · Best wrestler · Largest swarm · Longest-lived adult · Shortest larval stage · Best kicker · Most organised society · Most unsavoury defecation behaviour · Shortest-lived adult · Most explosive insect · Longest sperm · Largest parasite · Highest heat tolerance · Most diverse life histories · Most bizarre reverse metamorphosis · Longest larval stage · Best jumper · Best dancer · Best thief · Most patient insect · Best sunbathing protection · Most widespread insect

Most punctual insect

NAME   **periodical cicada** *Magicicada septendecim*

LOCATION   eastern North America

ATTRIBUTE   times mass adult emergence precisely after 17 years underground

Periodical cicadas make a mass emergence every 17 years precisely. *Magicicada septendecim* is the largest and most common of three cicada species with a 17-year life cycle (there are also four species with 13-year cycles). For 16 years and 11 months, the cicada nymphs feed out of sight in the ground, sucking the root sap from a wide range of trees and shrubs (but never conifers). In the designated April they push up near the soil surface and wait in a small burrow while their bodies undergo a final metamorphosis: dramatic chemical and physiological changes cause the body tissues to be rearranged in preparation for adulthood.

The precise signal to emerge is still not known, but all the cicadas in one area start to appear at the same time, often on the same night or two. They push up into the air, climb a short distance up a tree trunk or plant stem and split open along their backs so the adult insects can emerge. At first soft and white, the adults soon harden and darken and expand their wings. Then the males start singing. A week or so after emerging, mating takes place and each female lays 400–600 eggs in slits cut into twigs and branches. When the eggs hatch, the nymphs drop to the ground and burrow into the soil, gone for another 17 years.

This is a time of feasting for local birds (and fish), but the adult cicadas find enough safety in numbers for the remaining two or three weeks of their lives. Throughout eastern North America each locality has its own synchronised population of cicadas. These have been numbered since 1893 as generations (or 'broods') I to XVII. Each state or county has its own regular 17-year major cicadafest, but the next big countrywide emergence, from Pennsylvania to North Carolina, Arkansas, Indiana, Michigan and Ohio, will be the generation X in 2021.

On a hot sunny day, the smooth surface of a pond is broken by a series of wild ripples, twisting and contorting the otherwise flat water. Close examination shows that a group of shiny black beetles are whirring back and forth in random spirals and deranged zigzags. These are whirligig beetles, and their antics are no more random than they are deranged.

Although they can dive down into the water and fly off into the air, whirligigs spend almost their entire lives on the surface film. For this 'in between' life, they have four eyes, or rather their two eyes have each split and migrated so that the upper portions look out into the air and the lower ones down into the water.

Whirligigs move swiftly across the water by using their oar-shaped middle and hind legs as sculls, adjusting the angle of the legs during forward and back strokes just as rowers twist their oars. With 50 to 60 strokes per second, the little beetles can reach speeds of 25 cm/s (about 1 km/h or just over ½ mph).

The beetles' whirling behaviour is a useful means of evading predators. The confusing glints caused by the reflected sun, added to the lack of any clear trajectory to be anticipated, make the beetles extremely difficult to catch. As they move, the beetles detect the ripple 'echoes' bouncing back from pond plants and from each other. A whirligig is so good at this, it can swim up a 'lane' between two wires so close together that the beetle only just fits, without touching either of them.

Giddiest insect

NAME	**whirligig beetles** in the genus *Gyrinus*
LOCATION	worldwide
ABILITY	to whirl about in a confusing and erratic motion

Most useful young

NAME **weaver ants** in the genus *Oecophylla*

LOCATION sub-Saharan Africa, Southeast Asia, Australia

ATTRIBUTE use silk made by their larvae to glue leaf nests together

When naturalist Joseph Banks visited Australia with Captain Cook in 1768, he was fascinated by the green weaver ants that 'built a nest, in size between that of a man's head and his fist, by bending the leaves together, and gluing them with whitish paperish substances which held them firmly together.' What Banks did not know is that the whitish paperish substance he had observed was silk, and that it had been laid down by the ants using their larvae like glue-sticks.

Nest construction starts with an individual worker turning back a portion of a leaf on itself, gripping the leaf edge in its jaws. Other workers join in, using their jaws to grip the same leaf edge or to hold the waist of the ant ahead. Then, from a nearby nest, other workers bring out their nearly fully grown larvae. Holding one in its jaws, an ant presses the head of the grub down onto the first leaf. The grub squeezes out a droplet of silk from special glands in its head and, as the ant lifts it away, the silk is extruded into a thin fibre, instantly changing from liquid to solid. The grub is then touched onto the second leaf, creating a silk glue strand. Working backwards and forwards between the two leaves, the ant and its living maggot shuttle weave a network of many thousands of strands, which firmly fix the leaves together.

Each leaf nest is just one small unit within a single large weaver colony that may spread over several trees and total half a million ants. Silk is metabolically expensive to produce, and only two ant species have evolved this remarkable behaviour: *Oecophylla smaragdina*, found from India to Australia, and *O. longinoda* in tropical Africa.

Best mutual coexistence

NAME **ant-house plants** *Myrmecodia* species,
and their ant occupants *Iridiomyrmex cordatus*
LOCATION Southeast Asia and Australia
ATTRIBUTE a living house is fed by its tenants

In the tropical rainforests of Indomalaysia and Australia, strange football-sized warts grow on tree trunks and branches. In cross-section, they reveal a honeycomb network of chambers and passages inhabited by ants. But the ants did not build or hollow out the tunnels. They have been provided by a grateful plant, and in exchange, the ants nourish and protect their living quarters.

Myrmecodia is an epiphyte, which clings to the branch of a tree, often high up in the canopy of the forest, where it benefits from increased sunlight. But this precarious existence brings its own problems. The roots absorb some rainwater trapped in the spongy moss, but there are no soil nutrients available. *Myrmecodia* must have those delivered.

The stem of *Myrmecodia* is swollen into a large tuber-like structure and contains a labyrinth of spaces, called domatia, which attract ants to nest. The outer chambers are lined with tough, hard-wearing cells and it is here that the ants rear their brood. Pores aerate the cells and regulate the internal temperature. Towards the centre of the tuber, the cavities are dotted all over with small warty growths, inside which the ants dump the remains of their prey.

The plant actively absorbs nutrients from the decomposing ant refuse. These include phosphate, sulphate and nitrogen products, precisely the nutrients that other plants take from the soil, and without which the *Myrmecodia* could not grow. With the aid of its insect gardeners, *Myrmecodia* can colonise particularly harsh environments, and is often the first epiphyte to grow on a tree.

Largest overwintering congregation

NAME **convergent ladybird** *Hippodamia convergens*
LOCATION North America
ABILITY creates overwintering clusters of many millions of individuals

A ladybird's brightly patterned wings have inspired nursery rhymes, folklore and children's toys. But their distinctive colouring is more than mere decoration. The iconic ladybird, *Coccinella septempunctata*, is red with seven black spots, but there are plenty of other variations, including species that are yellow with black spots, black with red spots or orange with white spots. The strong colours are a warning to birds and other would-be predators that these beetles are not a tasty snack. If picked up in beak or jaws, ladybirds squeeze out their bright yellow or orange bitter-tasting haemolymph (the insect equivalent of blood) through special pores in their knees. The lesson is soon learned.

During winter, ladybirds huddle together in knots and clusters, and this emphasises their colourful warning signs. Most ladybird species gather in small groups of a few dozen or a hundred against a piece of rough tree bark or under dead leaves, but the convergent ladybird, *Hippodamia convergens*, converges in rock cavities and small caves in quantities that can be shovelled with a spade. Ladybirds are valued as aphid (greenfly) predators, and *H. convergens* is collected by the bucket-load from its winter quarters and sold to gardeners as a biocontrol agent. One congregation so harvested was estimated to be 500 gallons at 60 to 80,000 ladybirds per gallon – 30 to 40 million beetles gathered in one place.

Hippodamia convergens occurs throughout most of North America and is a common garden and meadow species. Both adults and larvae eat aphids but towards the end of summer, when hot dry weather reduces their prey, they migrate to the cooler valleys and canyons in hills and mountains. As poor weather sets in they are close to the rocky hollows in which they will spend the winter.

Early arrivers at a suitable shelter site release a 'safety' pheromone (chemical scent), which attracts more ladybirds to join the group. The pheromone lingers all year so subsequent generations of ladybirds are attracted to the same sites year on year, their pheromone releases constantly reinforcing the attractiveness of the cavities.

Unfortunately for the gardeners that buy the beetles, the ladybirds' first act on being released is usually to fly away. Their instincts tell them that they must fly down from the mountains to find food.

By gathering together in large numbers, insects can create large nests within which complex social behaviours develop. Colonial nesting occurs in many insects, but nothing can beat the vast conglomerations of the New World leafcutter ants.

These abundant ants cut leaf segments and carry them back to their nests. Here they chew the plant fragments into smaller pieces, fertilise them with their faeces and grow microscopic fungi that they later harvest for food. The nests are subterranean, with tunnels and chambers reaching 6 m (20 ft) down into the soil. The largest colonies found to date belong to the South American *Atta sexdens*, with estimates of between 5 and 8 million workers.

The huge colonies are founded by a single queen ant. Before leaving the nest in which she was reared, she collects a small wad of fungal material from one of the fungus 'garden' chambers and tucks it into a small pouch in her mouth. She flies off, mates with one or more male ants, casts off her wings and excavates a small new nest burrow. To start, she harvests her own cut leaves and inoculates them with the fungus wad. Eventually her worker offspring (sterile and relatively short-lived females) take over all the cutting, gardening and brood-tending duties, leaving her to the single occupation of laying eggs.

Leafcutter colonies survive for 10 to 15 years, during which time a queen will lay nearly 30,000 eggs a day and have as many as 200 million offspring. In one year in one mature, but not especially large, *Atta* colony, workers collected 4,550 sq m (49,000 sq ft) of leaf.

Largest colony

NAME	**leafcutter ants** in the genus *Atta*
LOCATION	Central and South America
ABILITY	create single coordinated colonies of up to 8 million individuals

Care of offspring by males is relatively common in vertebrates, but almost unknown in insects. Donation of food items during mating is a more common type of male nurturing behaviour. These nuptial gifts, as they are rather coyly called by naturalists, are given to the female by a male that wants to mate with her. In a few fiercely predatory fly species, there may be a measure of self-protection involved in giving the larger female something to eat while the smaller male impregnates her. However, the cannibalism often portrayed in insects (mating mantids, for example) is rare and usually occurs only under the stress of captivity.

The most accepted explanation is that by providing his mate with additional nutrition during the exhausting process of egg generation, a male is conferring an advantage on the offspring he will sire through her. Nutritious gifts vary from captured prey in scorpionflies to small seeds in ground bugs and regurgitated plant juices in flies and wasps. It is in the katydids and crickets, however, that gifts are most developed.

In many of these grasshopper-like creatures, the usually trivial expense of sexual insemination is greatly increased by the additional delivery of a large gelatinous body called a spermatophylax. The 19th-century French entomologist Jean Henri Fabre perfectly described one as 'an opalescent bag similar in size and colour to a mistletoe berry'. This valuable protein secretion is then eaten by the female.

As well as giving the female extra nutrients, this peculiar mechanism may have originated as a means of plugging her genitalia, keeping the delivered sperm inside the female's body and at the same time preventing other males from diluting it with their own. Studies indicate that the larger the spermatophylax, the longer a female will spend eating it before contemplating another mate.

In one group, the hump-winged crickets, the spermatophylax is not enough. In a unique turn of events, it is the female insect that mounts the male. She then starts to nibble his specialized pad-like back wings, also lapping up the dribbling haemolymph (the insect equivalent of blood). The male may get only one chance at mating. Once his wings have gone he is no longer very attractive to females no matter how large his next spermatophylax might be.

Most generous nuptial gift

NAME **male hump-winged crickets** in the genus *Cyphoderris*

LOCATION North America

ABILITY allow a female to eat a portion of their body, and some of their sperm package

Best passenger

NAME   **minims, smallest caste of leafcutter ants** in the genus *Atta*

LOCATION Central and South America

ABILITY   ride 'shotgun' on cut leaf fragments to prevent attacks of parasitic flies

Leafcutter ants, *Atta* species, are among the most numerous and important herbivorous insects in subtropical Central and South America. They create huge nests with millions of occupants (see page 128) and are active throughout the plant layer from the forest floor to the treetop canopy. With all this protein walking about it is not surprising that they are also subject to attack from a wide range of predators and parasites.

One of the most insidious attacks comes from small flies in the genus *Neodohrniphora*. The fly lays its eggs inside an ant's large head. The maggot that hatches proceeds to eat the ant alive, from the inside. The flies sit and wait on perches alongside a well-worn ant trail. When one has picked out a target, it approaches, stealthily, from behind, hovering above the ant before making its sudden, darting egg-laying manoeuvre. In one study it was estimated that 2.2% of ants on a foraging trail were parasitised by *Neodohrniphora*.

If an ant becomes aware of the aggressor it tries to out-run it, or sits back, squatting on the ground and waving its antennae and front legs wildly in the air. This defence appears to work well, but the ants are especially vulnerable on the return part of their foraging journey, when they are heading back to the nest weighed down with a piece of cut leaf much larger than themselves. For this part of the journey, they recruit help.

The very smallest workers in the colony, called minims, are a fraction of the size of the large leafcutting hordes. Inside the subterranean nest their main task is to patrol the fungus 'gardens', weeding them by pulling out strands and spores of alien mould. But often they are picked up by their larger sisters and carried off to the leaf-harvesting territory, up to 50 m (160 ft) away. On the return journey, the minims ride on the upper edge of the cut leaves and ward off the fly attacks. Since they are so small they are unlikely to be targeted by the flies, but offer a good defence to the burden-carrying ant below.

Most necrophilic insect

NAME   **burying beetles** in the genus *Nicrophorus* and other species

LOCATION   different species worldwide

ABILITY   carefully burying the bodies of small birds and mammals

Carrion is a valuable resource, and one that is exploited by a large and diverse range of scavengers. Largest and most spectacular among the insect corpse visitors are the often brightly barred orange and black burying beetles, also called sextons after the warden who cares for a churchyard and digs graves. After blowflies, burying beetles are usually the first to arrive at the body of a recently deceased small mammal or bird, detecting the subtle chemical changes that come with the onset of decay. There is great competition for the small body of a mouse or sparrow, and the beetles fight over their prize. Eventually one pair, usually the largest male and female, are left. If a lone male finds a corpse unoccupied he climbs up and adopts a tail-up position, releasing a chemical scent to attract a mate.

Working together, male and female use their stout, broad legs to excavate the soil from beneath the body, pushing the spoil up into heaps all around. After several hours the body slowly slips down into the void they have dug beneath it, and the loose soil heaped up crumbles back down to bury the corpse. Out of sight, with the smell of decay masked, the treasure belongs to the beetles.

Burying beetles are among the few insects where both parents care for the brood. After securing and hiding a corpse, the female lays eggs in the soil around it. The parents then eat from the decaying flesh and regurgitate partly digested food for their grubs to feed on when they emerge. Eventually the growing larvae will be able to feed themselves as the corpse decomposes to become putrescent and liquefied.

Burying beetles have to compete with blowflies, which lay their fast-developing eggs before the beetles arrive or while they are digging the grave. To counter this, the beetles carry small mites attached to their bodies, picked up from the corpse on which they fed as maggots. The mites do no harm to the beetles. They are hitching a lift to their next meal – blowfly eggs and larvae.

The oldest trap in the world is a very simple one: dig a large deep hole, then wait and see what falls into it. Antlions, the voracious larvae of delicate lacy-winged insects that look like fragile dragonflies, take this elementary technique and transform it into a marvellous feat of engineering.

The pit they construct is perfectly conical. The sides are at precisely the right angle to remain stable until they are disturbed, when they collapse, bringing the unfortunate victim sliding down to the bottom. At the very bottom of the pit is the antlion, waiting with open scimitar-sharp jaws to dispatch its prey. As their name suggests, antlions feed mainly on ants, but they will take whatever they can get. They live mainly in dry sandy areas, making their trap pits in the shelter of overhanging rocks or trees, and avoiding areas where rain might dampen the soil. The dry sand is the secret to their pitfall design.

To make its conical pit, the antlion backs into the ground tail first and slowly spirals round until only the head and curved jaws are visible. Using one of its front legs it scoops a small pile of sand grains onto its flat head and then flicks them away. It continues scooping and flicking while spiralling round and round, and as the sand is jettisoned, the pit gradually takes on its distinctive conical form. When the pit is completed, the antlion remains motionless, invisible under a single layer of sand grains at the bottom.

The sloping sides of the trap are at what civil engineers describe as the angle of repose. In other words they are on the verge of imminent collapse. When an ant stumbles over the crest, the sides give way under it, and it starts to slide downwards. If the ant is able to make headway up the crumbling slope, the antlion starts flicking head-loads of sand up at it. This has the combined effect of knocking the ant downhill and undermining the sides of the pit to make them collapse faster. Once caught by the antlion, the ant is dragged under the sand to stifle its struggling, and its innards are sucked out.

Cleverest digger

NAME **antlions** larvae in the genus *Myrmeleon* and other species
LOCATION worldwide
ABILITY dig the perfect pitfall trap to catch their unwary ant prey

Most violent sex act

NAME   **honeybee** *Apis mellifera*

LOCATION   originally Europe, Africa, Asia; introduced worldwide by humans

ATTRIBUTE   males willingly consent to fatal castration during mating

The commonest sexual urge for males is to mate often, with as many females as possible, to ensure some paternity of the next generation. Females, on the other hand, are assured of maternity and are able to choose a single male from a selection on offer. But in the honeybee, things are very different.

The difference can be seen from the moment a virgin queen leaves the nest in search of drones (male honeybees): in most insects it is the males that actively seek out females. Previously the drones will have congregated around prominent local landmarks such as treetops and large bushes.

As soon as the drones catch sight or scent of the queen, they pursue her, with dozens or even hundreds of males joining in. This spectacular mating throng is known as a drone comet because of its shape as it moves through the air. Inside the flying cloud, individual males attempt to mount the queen, approaching her from below.

Once he has grasped the queen in his legs, the male inserts the inflatable penetrative portion of his genitalia, called the endophallus, into her. He then relinquishes his grip and flips backwards, caught by the rush of air. This sudden flexing of his body compresses his internal organs, causing an explosive release of sperm, and at the same time the endophallus snaps off with an audible pop. The castrated drone falls to the ground and dies. The queen retains the male genitalia, which is easily visible protruding from the tip of her abdomen and is called the 'mating sign' by beekeepers.

One male may not be enough for the queen. During a life of up to five years, she may lay a million or more eggs, all fertilised by sperm stored in her body from the half-hour nuptials of the drone comet. Despite the blocking presence of the mating sign in the queen's genitalia, a second male can scoop out a broken endophallus (and some of the sperm) and insert his own. A queen normally mates two or three times, but may mate up to 20 times.

Wild rose bushes (usually field rose, *Rosa arvensis*, and dog rose, *Rosa canina*) are sometimes decorated along their stems by strange, crimson, furry growths that look like tangles of red wool or moss filaments. The growths are called bedeguar, from the Persian *bad-awar*, meaning 'wind-brought'. The name appears to be the result of a confusion with the fluffy wind-blown seeds of thistles, which they sometimes resemble.

In fact, the tangled feathery mass is grown directly from leaf buds on the rose stem. It starts out the same green as the leaves, but later matures to bright red. The bedeguar is made by the rose, but the plant has no control over its destiny in this case. Its normal metabolism and growth patterns have been completely usurped by the tiny creatures growing within.

The process starts when a 4-mm-long (⅛-in) insect, *Diplolepis rosae*, lays its 40–60 eggs into the bud, along with a cocktail of chemicals. Instead of developing into a new rose leaf stem, the bud grows into a stout bulbous wart covered with twisted hairs. As the eggs hatch and the maggots start to feed inside the wart, they continue to secrete similar growth-commandeering substances. Eventually the heart of the bedeguar will be 30 mm (1.2 in) across, the size of a walnut; the fleecy tendrils will stretch to tennis-ball size.

This corruption of normal plant growth to create a protective and nutritious environment for the grubs is common, and many invertebrate species create their own distinctive dwellings, called galls, on their own targeted plant species. Some are very small, housing just a single individual gall-former; others, including the bedeguar, are communal.

Like all communities, the bedeguar is home to more than just its creator occupants, as thieves and freeloaders are also attracted to the shelter and abundant food supply it provides. Many of these 'guests', more correctly called inquilines, do little or no harm to the *Diplolepis* grubs. However, others are parasitoids, which lay their eggs in the *Diplolepis* larvae (and also in the larvae of the guests) and whose maggots then proceed to eat them all alive. These parasitoids are themselves attacked by their own parasitoids (called hyperparasitoids). So complex is the bedeguar gall community that 25 different insect species have been reared from these strange plant growths.

Biggest plant distortion

NAME	**bedeguar or robin's pin-cushion** *Diplolepis rosae*
LOCATION	Europe
ABILITY	chemically distorts a plant's growth patterns to create a nursery for its young

Best thermometer

NAME **snowy tree cricket** *Oecanthus fultoni*

LOCATION North America

ABILITY sings in tune to the air temperature

The repeated chirring songs of crickets are the iconic sound of the quiet rural scene as dusk falls and the wind drops. They are dubbed onto movies and radio plays to set the scene, and feature widely on relaxation CDs. Although some cricket songs are very melodious, their real purpose is to communicate – males singing to females.

There are over 20,000 species of crickets, katydids and grasshoppers in the world, each with its own unique song. It was once thought that the song of each species was fixed, but in 1897 American inventor Thomas Dolbear published his observation that the calls of the snowy tree cricket, *Oecanthus fultoni*, varied according to the ambient air temperature.

Dolbear's law stated that the air temperature, in degrees Fahrenheit, is the number of calls during 15 seconds plus 40 (to calculate Celsius take the number of calls during 8 seconds and add 5). It worked remarkably well, earning the insect the name thermometer cricket.

It has since been discovered that the thermometer cricket varies across the USA, singing at a slightly slower rate in the east compared to the west. In the west, the closely related Riley's tree cricket, *Oecanthus rileyi*, sings a similar song, so the snowy tree cricket speeds up so as not to get confused.

The now-accepted formulae are as follows:

In the east:
(calls in 13 secs) + 40 [°F] or (calls in 7 secs) + 5 [°C]

In the west:
(calls in 12.5 secs) + 38 [°F] or (calls in 7 secs) + 4 [°C]

Best architect

NAME **termites** in the genus *Macrotermes*

LOCATION sub-Saharan Africa

ABILITY build climate-controlled skyscrapers

The flat, scrubby grasslands of the African savannah are everywhere punctuated with tall mud structures as hard as concrete. These are no mere heaps of earth. They are structurally engineered cities with industrial and residential zones, climate control and air conditioning. And they are built by tiny termites.

Among the most amazing, and best studied, are the nests of *Macrotermes michaelseni* in southern Africa. Each nest has three distinct but overlapping structures. At the top is a narrow spire sometimes reaching as high as 9 m (30 ft). This sits on a broad conical base 4–5 m (13–16 ft) in diameter and 1.5 m (5 ft) high. Around this is an 'outwash pediment' of soil eroded from the main mound, up to 20 m (65 ft) across.

From the outside, the mound looks impenetrable. The very outer layer is quite dusty and loose, but just beneath this is a hard shell of baked earth mixed with termite saliva. Inside, the mound is riddled with tunnels, galleries and voids. And although every nest is slightly different, they are all built to a regular blueprint.

In the very centre is a complex maze of narrow brood galleries where the termite eggs are kept and hatchlings fed.

Around these are larger tunnels where the termites grow their food. Termites use almost any cellulose plant material from leaf fragments, fruit and seeds, to pieces of dead wood. They bring it back to the nest and add it to their compost. The termites then eat a fungus they cultivate on the rotting cellulose. When a colony is founded, by a male and female pair, they inoculate it with a morsel of fungus from their birth-nest. This fungus, *Termitomyces*, is found only inside termite nests and has evolved a symbiotic relationship with the termites.

From the centre of the brood chambers and fungus gardens, a large narrow void – the chimney – stretches up into the nest spire. It does not empty directly into the outside, but is linked to many narrow passages down the sides of the mound. The intricate arrangement of tunnels and chimney creates an air-conditioning unit for the entire nest. Warm air (30°C/86°F) thick with carbon dioxide (CO_2) rises up through the chimney. As the air passes out and into the peripheral tunnels, heat and CO_2 escape through the relatively thin walls of the mound spire, and oxygen passes in. The cooler air (now 24°C/75°F) sinks down into the nest 'cellar' and is drawn back up through the nest. These climate-controlled termite cities can last for a hundred years.

Cleverest drinker

NAME	**Namib darkling beetles** in the genus *Stenocara* and other species
LOCATION	Namibia
ABILITY	to collect and drink their own water in the driest place on Earth

The Namib Desert in southwest Africa is one of the driest places in the world, receiving less than 10 mm (½ in) of rainfall a year. The barren sand dunes are not, however, devoid of life. Scuttling across them is an assortment of round-bodied and long-legged beetles. Called darkling beetles, because of their semi-nocturnal habits, they are scavengers, and live mainly on wind-blown detritus, which is virtually the only food available to them. Their round bodies, tough skins and sun-dodging habits help reduce water loss, but even the most careful must drink sometimes. Darklings have evolved an ingenious means of collecting water.

Rain is rare here, but night fogs regularly drift in from the ocean. On foggy nights, the beetles rise up on their long legs and tilt their tails into the air. Slowly, the fog condenses onto the insect's body. The fog-condensing mechanism has been minutely studied in one particular genus, *Stenocara*. The wing cases of these beetles are covered with raised tubercles (rounded bumps). The tubercles attract water to their easily wetted (hydrophilic) surfaces. As the water droplets grow, they droop onto the spaces between the bumps. The gullies are covered with a waxy water-repellent (hydrophobic) layer, so when the droplet finally drips, it quickly runs down, just like rain running in a plastic gutter. Because of the tilt of the beetle's body, tail up and head down, the droplets drain down towards its mouth.

The Namib Desert is one of the oldest arid places on Earth, and has been desertified for 55 million years. In that time, Namibian darkling beetles have been able to diversify and today there are over 200 species there, many found nowhere else in the world.

Tiger beetles (*Cicindela* species) are voracious predators: fast (see page 96), agile and armed with sharp jaws. Their larvae are no less deadly. The tiger beetle grub excavates a vertical tunnel in loose soil. It then sits at the entrance, with its broad head blocking the hole and its jaws prised open, waiting like a living gin trap. Any small invertebrate walking over it is caught between the jaws, dragged underground and devoured.

Wherever there are tiger beetles, small slender ant-like insects will also be found. These insects have no common name, but many of them belong to the genus *Methoca*. They are related to wasps, and the males of some species are winged. Ants are typical prey for the tiger beetle grub, so when *Methoca* traipses over its head the beetle larva snaps its jaws shut as normal. But *Methoca*'s narrow waist is heavily armoured to protect it from the grub's jaws. Just as the beetle larva's head rises up to grip its would-be prey, the female wasp bends down and stings it in the soft, and now exposed, neck. The beetle grub immediately lets go its grip and withdraws into its burrow. *Methoca* waits a few moments for the paralysing venom to take effect then waltzes down into the burrow. A few more stings may be necessary to fully sedate the grub.

The female wasp now lays a single egg on the immobilised tiger beetle larva, on which her grub will feed. She then buries it by filling in the hole with loose sand and soil. The normally fatal bite from the tiger beetle grub appears to have no effect on *Methoca*. She sets off in search of more burrows and repeats her daredevil egg-laying strategy again and again.

Most dangerous egg-laying strategy

NAME	*Methoca articulata* and other species
LOCATION	different species worldwide
ABILITY	allows herself to be bitten so that she can lay her eggs

Most adventurous insect

NAME **sea-skaters** in the genus *Halobates*
LOCATION Atlantic, Indian and Pacific Oceans
ABILITY lives on the open ocean, the harshest habitat on Earth

The most difficult and dangerous habitat in the insect world is not a searing-hot desert, desolate mountain or polluted city. It is the open ocean. Of the approximately one million different insect species known to date, only five are truly oceanic.

Called sea-skaters, these adventurous animals closely resemble the pond-skaters that commonly zip about on the surface of freshwater pools and streams, and probably evolved from them many millions of years ago. They have a small body perched on long, thin legs. The front legs are short and stout, adapted for grasping, and are thought to be used to grip prey when feeding. Middle and hind legs are stilt-like and fringed with long hairs that rest on the surface tension of the water, holding the insect up in the air. The middle pair act like oars, powering the sea-skater along, while the back pair are used to steer.

About 45 species in the genus *Halobates* are known. They are all tropical, but most are inshore dwellers, often found in the shelter of mangrove swamps. Only five species have ventured out into the deep sea, three in the Pacific, one in the Indian and Pacific, and one across the Atlantic, Indian and Pacific Oceans.

Sea-skaters live in such an inaccessible place that very little has been discovered about their biology, life history or habits. Keeping them in observation tanks is difficult, so details of breeding seasons, growth rates and behaviour are all very sketchy.

All sea-skaters are dull silvery grey because they are covered with fine water-repellent hairs to prevent their becoming waterlogged. Their body structure, similar to pond-skaters', is adapted to surface living, so they cannot dive into the water. They have no wings. Sea-skaters have been found feeding on zooplankton, fish eggs and fry, and a dead jellyfish. Their eggs have been found glued to floating objects such as logs, bird feathers, seaweed and lumps of tar. It seems that egg-laying sites may be few and far between out at sea. Human litter is often favoured. In 2002, an empty plastic milk container was dredged from the middle of the Pacific Ocean with 70,000 sea-skater eggs attached to it. In the same net were found 833 specimens of *Halobates sobrinus*.

There was a time when cows grazing quietly in a meadow would suddenly all raise their tails and bolt off to the other side of the field in a great harum-scarum stampede. This gadding about, as the panic was called, was instigated by an insect resembling a small bumblebee. The cows knew that pain and suffering awaited them if the gad-fly had its way.

The furry brown and orange fly that engendered such panic, the ox warble, is known throughout the northern hemisphere wherever cattle graze. In pursuing the cows, it is not trying to bite them, but to lay its small, oval white eggs on the hairs on the animals' legs and flanks. The larvae, which hatch quickly, wriggle down to the skin, then puncture it and burrow underneath. There they feed on the blood and flesh, secreting enzymes to break down the muscle and fat.

For several months over autumn the larvae migrate underneath the skin of the animal, moving upwards towards the backbone. Eventually they grow to the size and hardness of marbles, giving the cow the appearance of being covered all over its back with small bumps. These bumps, called warbles, are now open wounds, where the maggot has cut a breathing hole. This can lead to infection, as dribbling pus and blood ooze from the cut. Eventually the pressure of festering liquid under the warble pushes the larva out from the cow's hide and it falls to the ground, where it pupates to transform into an adult fly.

The ox warble has been the bane of farmers ever since oxen were domesticated in prehistoric times. The stockmen were not overly worried about the pain inflicted on their stock. Meat produce and milk were hardly affected (although the gadding made the cows irritable at milking time), but the leather was pock-marked and holed by the ravages of the warble-worms. Treatments were draconian, ranging from highly toxic mercurial ointments to lavish smears of cart grease laced with sulphur, turpentine, linseed oil and tar.

Gad-flies are now mostly gone from the domestic stock of North America and Europe. They have been largely eradicated by the use of insecticide pastes, pills and tonics given in the cattle feed. They still occur in wild bison and buffalo, which can be seen gadding about in a vain attempt to escape the attentions of this horrible insect.

Most disgusting habits

NAME **ox warble fly** *Hypoderma bovis*
LOCATION Europe, northern Asia and North America
ABILITY larva burrows into the living flesh of cattle

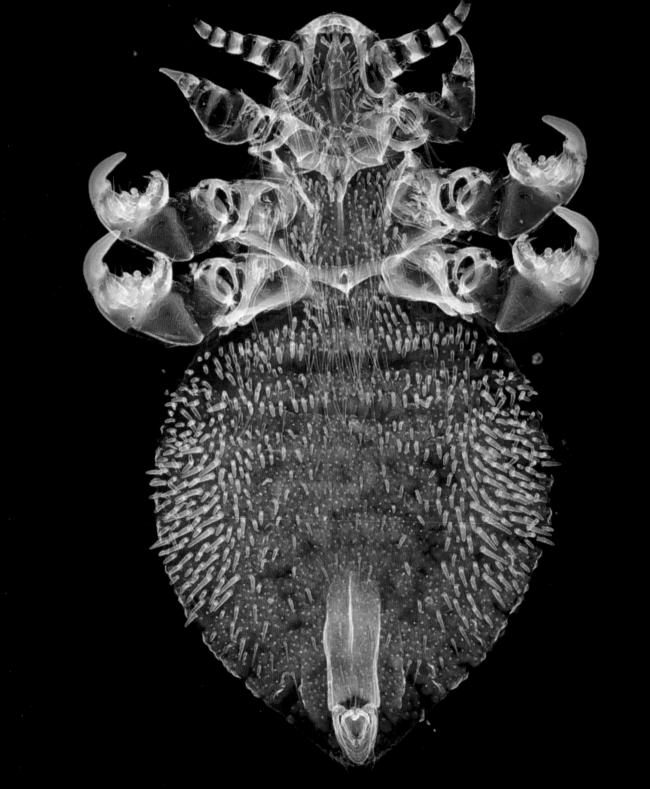

Most cold-tolerant insect

NAME   **Weddell seal louse** *Antarctophthirus ogmorhini*

LOCATION   Antarctica

ABILITY   to survive months in Antarctic seas at subzero temperatures

Truly cold-adapted insects are very rare but the Weddell seal louse, *Antarctophthirus agmorhini*, is definitely worthy of the title. This tiny (3-mm) relative of head and crab lice (see pages 272 and 252) occurs only on its host animal, attached to hairs on the tail, ankles, hips and hind flippers. The Weddell seal, *Leptonychotes weddellii*, lives around Antarctica. It spends much of its time swimming below the ice, only coming up to breathe through blowholes, so the lice are more or less constantly exposed to temperatures of -2°C (28°F). They also have to suffer huge compression as the seals dive up to 450 m (1,500 ft) down for over an hour at a time. A close relative, *A. microchir* (pictured left), suffers similar hardships on Patagonian sea lions.

The seals only spend significant time out of the water between September and November, when they haul themselves out to mate and have pups. The louse is nevertheless able to survive, and even thrive, and all Weddell seals are infested to greater or lesser degree. During the cold-enforced inactivity, the lice just hang on. Cold water has more oxygen dissolved in it than warm water and the lice aborb enough of it to keep them alive. They also have overlapping scales on their bodies, which trap a thin layer of air.

The lice feed, by taking blood meals, when their hosts' diving and hunting activity makes the seals warm up enough to dissipate heat, increasing blood flow to the outer skin layer of the tail and flippers. During the seals' short breeding period, the lice have a brief respite in which to mate and lay their own eggs. This is a relatively warm period of the insect's life cycle, but their eggs are still able to hatch at temperatures of 0–4°C (32–41°F), and the louse's other life processes take place at 5–15°C (43–59°F), much cooler than insects elsewhere.

Most devious prey trap

NAME **Australasian glow-worms**
in the genus *Arachnocampa*

LOCATION Australia and New Zealand

ABILITY glow in the dark to lure prey
to a sticky death

In the dark caves of Australia and New Zealand, tiny glowing lights decorate the ceilings like animated constellations. Called glow-worms, because they glow and are worm-like, they are not related to the beetles of the northern hemisphere that share the name. They are fly larvae, and they do not glow to find each other: they glow to attract their food.

The glow-worms are long, thin maggots and they attach themselves to the cave roof inside a slim silk and mucus tube. From this they dangle down 30 to 70 silk threads, 50–150 mm (2–6 in) long. They are named *Arachnocampa*, meaning spider maggot, after these silk strands. Each line is covered in glue droplets and looks like a dew-drop necklace.

Caves are inhospitable places, where nutrition is thin on the ground. But caves do often have flowing water and they offer shelter. Small insects wafted into the caves by air currents over the water, or taking temporary shelter, become disoriented in the darkness. Their natural inclination is to fly upwards or towards light, so they fly straight up to the sticky strands of the glow-worms.

Once ensnared, the victims' struggles simply get them even more tangled in the dangling glue strands, and they are soon subdued. Now the glow-worms reel in their catch – which may be flies, lacewings, bees, wasps, beetles or spiders – and devour it at their leisure. The larvae may wait in the darkness for days or weeks between these meals.

It can take up to a year for the larva to feed enough to mature into an adult. The adult flies do not survive long after their eggs are laid, and probably end up as food for the next generation of glow-worms.

Most untrusting sex act

NAME   **Apollo butterflies** in the genus *Parnassius*

LOCATION   circumpolar and montane regions in the northern hemisphere

ABILITY   a mating male attaches a biological chastity belt to the female

In most male insects there is one overriding urge – to mate with as many females as possible in order to sire as many offspring as possible. This often conflicts with the female's primary need, to select the best possible mate to father her progeny. This has given rise to a huge variety of often complex mating rituals and strategies. The Apollo butterflies have developed one of the most extreme evolutionary adaptations: the chastity belt.

There is little, if any, courtship between male and female Apollo butterflies. The male simply grabs a female and they mate. But rather than dashing off as quickly as possible to find another available female, the male stays with the female for several hours. The white and pale yellow wings, marked with black bars and red circles, warn potential predators that Apollos are poisonous and foul-tasting. The mating butterflies have little to fear and, almost uniquely among butterflies, if they are disturbed they just sit tight, apparently unwilling to fly away.

There is purpose in the butterflies' prolonged coitus. As well as transferring sperm to the female, the male is also secreting a liquid gel from special glands near the tip of his abdomen, which pop out during mating. This jelly solidifies into a pale pink or yellow mating plug called a sphragis. A biological chastity belt, the sphragis prevents further males mating with the female, although that doesn't stop them trying.

In population studies, the sphragis is a sure indication that a female has mated. Dissections show that, despite the attempts of further suitors, only one male ever mates successfully with each female. The effort (in terms of metabolic output) is huge for the male, which can produce only one or two sphragises during his brief adult life of a few weeks.

Best sculptor

NAME	**potter wasps** in the family Eumenidae
LOCATION	different species worldwide
ABILITY	create delicate urn-shaped mud flasks to rear their young

Good parenting is not often thought of as a typical insect attribute, but a remarkable number do more than simply lay their eggs and walk away. One of the best ways to improve the chances for any offspring is to leave them enough food to see them through larvahood. A few bees and wasps live in social colonies and build nests to achieve this. The majority of bees and wasps simply dig a crude burrow – or use somebody else's – put in some food, lay an egg, and go. These 'solitary' species (a lone female working alone) can be quite inventive, using hollow plant stems, holes in walls or even empty snail shells. But the most exquisite workmanship is displayed by the potter wasps, which build Grecian urns and amphorae for their young.

The wasp collects mud or clay and shapes it into small earthenware pots attached to stems, leaves or branches. Carrying a ball of damp soil between long jaws and front legs, the potter starts by attaching the base to a likely spot. As it dries and hardens, she slowly builds up the sides of the pot, daub by daub. Although the exterior appears rough and unfinished, the inside is smooth and crisp. The finishing touch is a flared rim on the small opening at the top, carefully manipulated with the jaws. Once the urn is nearly completed, the potter wasp sets out to hunt for caterpillars or beetle larvae. She stings her prey to paralyse them, then stuffs them into the container nest. She will lay a single egg in the clay vessel, suspended on a silk-like thread. She then seals up the hole, and starts on another pot nearby.

Protected and with a store of food, the potter larva has a very good chance of survival. Its mother has to be careful, though. Halfway through loading in caterpillars, her nest is vulnerable to brood parasites (usually other wasp species), which sneak in and lay their own eggs in the pot.

Most unusual foodstuff

NAME   **purple emperor butterfly** *Apatura iris*

LOCATION   Europe and northern Asia

ATTRIBUTE   a taste for dung, putrescent carrion and car exhaust

The purple emperor is a truly regal-looking butterfly. Its imperial upper side – iridescent purple marked with flashes of white – makes it one of the most handsome insects of the temperate zone, easily competing with some of the flashier tropical butterflies. It is a denizen of old mature woodlands, and while its streamlined green caterpillars feed on the leaves of willows and sallows, the adults are most often seen flying high around prominent oak and beech trees looking for mates.

Purple emperors do not visit flowers to feed on nectar, so close observation is often restricted to glimpses through a pair of binoculars. However, they do visit the ground to go mud-puddling – sitting on the damp mud beside streams, pools or puddles to drink. This habit, shared with many other butterflies, enables them to pick up essential minerals. In addition to pools of water, purple emperors will get their minerals from animal faeces, pools of urine, putrescent carrion or the dripping condensate from car exhaust pipes. The tip of the relatively stout yellow proboscis is armed with several hairy pads, which help the insect soak up liquids from the mud. Both males and females feed in this unusual way, and it is thought that they need the additional nutrients to mature sperm and eggs.

Elsewhere in the insect kingdom all sorts of other strange food choices can be found. The cigarette beetle, *Lasioderma serricorne*, eats dried tobacco leaves and is a sometime pest in stored cigarettes and cigars. Spider beetles, *Niptus hololeucus*, were found in their thousands in a laboratory bottle of casein (a protein found in milk) that had been sealed for over a decade. Silverfish, *Lepisma saccharina*, chew through wallpaper to get at the starch of the wallpaper paste behind. The larvae of museum beetles, *Anthrenus verbasci*, destroy stuffed animals and stored skins in museum collections, including drawers of pinned insect specimens in the entomology departments.

There is a general rule of thumb that insects have a more or less sedentary larval stage (the caterpillar, maggot or grub), which does all the eating and growing, and then an adult stage, which does the mating, migrating and egg-laying. This works well and everyone knows that a caterpillar turns into a butterfly (or a moth). In oil beetles, however, there are several completely different larval stages through which the animal passes, each adapted for a particular stage in the beetle's complex life cycle.

Oil beetles (so called because of their poisonous oily secretions; see page 228) lay their eggs in the soil, the root thatch of grass or on the herbage. From these eggs hatch tiny, active six-legged larvae called triungulins (meaning 'three-clawed' – uniquely among insects they have three claws on each foot rather than one or two). The slim and moderately long-legged triungulins climb to the top of a flower and wait to hitch a lift on a passing insect. They must wait for a particular insect because each species of oil beetle must reach the nest of usually just one particular species of wasp or bee.

Only a few triungulins are successfully picked up by the correct bee or wasp species and taken back to the host nest or brood cells. Here the triungulin transforms into a fat, short-legged grub. It feeds on the host egg and, depending on the oil beetle species, also any host food stores and neighbouring host larvae. When nearly fully grown, the oil beetle grub changes into a tough, almost legless maggot and may remain dormant for many months during the winter or dry season. Near the end of its larvahood, it changes again into a second grub form, excavates a pupal chamber and changes into a pupa (chrysalis). The adult will emerge at the correct time of year to ensure the availability of foraging wasps or bees for its own triungulin hatchlings.

The development through several different larval forms is called hypermetamorphosis. Oil beetles are particularly unusual in that they have two active dispersal stages – when they move from one habitat to another – during their life cycle: triungulin larva and adult.

Most extreme metamorphosis

NAME **oil beetles** in the family Meloidae
LOCATION worldwide
ATTRIBUTE different larval stages for different larval requirements

Best eyesight

NAME   **common green darner** *Anax junius*

LOCATION   North and Central America

ATTRIBUTE   highest visual acuity in the insect world

Unlike vertebrate eyes with their complex pupil and iris focusing mechanisms, insect visual systems are based on a simple non-moving structure that captures light from a very small portion of the sky. The light is directed onto a few light-sensitive cells, which in turn fire one or a few nerve impulses to the brain.

Called an ommatidium, the only eye part visible externally is the minute hexagonal lens. Beneath this is a long, tapering conical structure, called a rhabdom; down its centre are the light sensors that fire the nerves.

Many ommatidia are clustered together to form the complete insect eye. The dome shape of the 'compound' eye is formed by the tessellated hexagonal lenses. The visual image constructed inside the insect's brain is a mosaic of overlapping micro-images, each ommatidial signal resembling a single brush-stroke on an Impressionist painting, or maybe a single pixel in a digital camera. The larger the number of ommatidia, the finer the resolution of the image.

The largest eyes in the insect world belong to dragonflies, especially the large and powerful hawkers (also called darners because of their needle-like bodies). These are commonly claimed to have 30,000 ommatidia in each eye. Not many species have been individually checked, but one research project counted 29, 247 in the eye of the common green darner.

The dragonfly's interpretation of the world is less a photographic view of the scenery below and more a recognition of shapes, patterns and movement. The ommatidia are arranged in bands and patches of different sizes, with different focuses and different resolutions, some for prey detection at close range, others for predator-spotting at a distance.

There are many species of insects that lack eyes altogether. Of those with eyes, the insect with the worst eyesight must be a small ant, *Hypoponera punctatissima*, which has but one ommatidium for each eye.

Best mimic

NAME	**African mocker swallowtail** *Papilio dardanus*
LOCATION	Africa, Madagascar and southern Arabia
ABILITY	mimics many different poisonous butterflies across its geographic range

When Victorian naturalist and scientist Walter Henry Bates explored the Amazon in the 1840s and 50s he found large numbers of brightly coloured and slow-flying *Heliconius* butterflies. Having eaten toxic plants as caterpillars, the adult butterflies were poisonous, or at least distasteful, to birds, and could afford to be conspicuous and leisurely. What amazed him most was a completely different series of non-toxic *Dismorphia* butterflies, which were identically patterned to the poisonous *Heliconius*. He surmised that the edible butterflies gained protection from predators by mimicking the wing patterns of those that were chemically protected. This concept is now known as Batesian mimicry.

Mimicry is widespread in the insect world: hoverflies mimic bees and wasps, bugs mimic ants, caterpillars mimic bird droppings, butterflies mimic each other. It is often possible to match precisely the harmless mimic species with the toxic, noxious or otherwise dangerous 'model' species, and many Batesian butterfly pairs are well known. And just as some butterflies have slightly different patterns and colours across their wide geographic ranges, so the mimics keep pace with these slight racial changes. As Bates travelled upriver he had to examine every butterfly to see which was which.

The African mocker swallowtail, *Papilio dardanus*, is the master mimic. Across its huge continental range it mimics at least 14 different distasteful model butterflies. At least the females do. The males, throughout Africa, are all black and pale yellow, with the hind wing tails that give the butterfly its name. Some females mimic the African monarch, *Danaus chrysippus*, which is broadly orange, fringed with black and with prominent white flashes across the tips of the front wings. Others closely resemble the Layman butterfly, *Amauris albimaculata*, which is black with a few white spots on the front wings and a pale yellow patch on the hind wings. Yet others are identical to the friar butterfly, *Amauris niavius*, which is black with large patches of pale blue-white. None of these models has wing tails, so female mockers lack them too.

A final twist comes in Madagascar. Here female *P. dardanus* are the same colour and shape as the males – black and yellow with those prominent wing tails. It may be that the evolution of mimicry on mainland Africa began only after the Malagasy population was separated when tectonic plate movements moved this island away into the Indian Ocean during the Jurassic period, 208–146 million years ago.

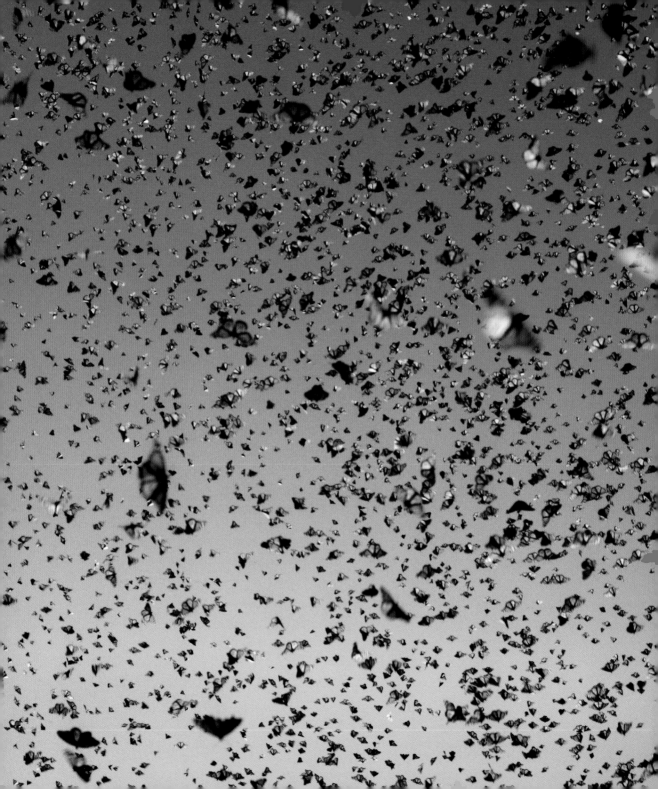

Biggest migration

NAME **monarch butterfly** *Danaus plexippus* *

LOCATION North America

ATTRIBUTE an annual autumn pilgrimage of up to 5,200 km (3,200 miles), returning the following spring

Around the beginning of September each year, the monarch butterflies east of the Rocky Mountains, something in the region of 250 million of them, start feeding avidly to build up reserves, increasing their body weights by as much as 30 per cent. Then they start to fly south. Starting from southern Canada and the USA around the Great Lakes they must average about 80 km (50 miles) each day. We do not know how they navigate, but most routes appear to funnel through Texas, and by November they have arrived at a scattering of about 30 sheltered valleys in the mountains west of Mexico City.

The butterflies settle in the bushes and oyamel fir trees, fold their wings together and hang in hibernation torpor for the winter. On sunny mornings some of the roosting butterflies fly down to take water from nearby streams, then return to the trees with the cool of sunset. Everywhere the skies are alive with butterflies and the trees bend under the weight of the insects.

In February, temperatures are rising and day length is increasing. These triggers initiate mating, and by March coupled butterflies are everywhere. Within days, the females start to leave. The males die soon after mating. The flight back is not as coordinated as the move south. As the butterflies head north they lay eggs on their foodplants, milkweeds. The caterpillars feed up, pupate and emerge as adults to spread farther north with each generation.

By August, the monarchs flying in southern Ontario are probably the fourth generation, the great-grandchildren, of the butterflies that left Mexico five months earlier. Soon they will start the southward flight, and even though they have no 'memory' of their ancestors' travels, they make the same journey, follow the same routes, roost in the same trees during overnight stops, and end up in the same few valleys near Mexico City. How this remarkable migration is achieved is still mostly a mystery.

* **Stop Press** See page 288 for the latest news on this record.

When males and females of the same species look very different, sex is usually at the bottom of it. Fighting over females has given males formidable weapons or bizarre forms. Alternatively, females have concentrated their energies on building a huge egg-laying mass, leaving tiny males to find them using chemical scents. Many of these strange forms and extraordinary shapes have a self-evident purpose, but in the harlequin beetle it took nearly 250 years to discover why the males needed such long front legs.

Acrocinus longimanus is a handsome and striking insect. Its beautifully marked brown and yellow harlequin body gives it the common name it so richly deserves. It has long been sought by collectors and dealers of exotic insects. But what is most striking about it is the extreme discrepancy between the leg lengths of male and female.

In the largest males, up to 7.5 cm (3 in) long, the front legs can reach 15 cm (6 in). In the few females that approach this large body size, the front legs don't reach half this length. The front legs of large males are also sharply hooked at the ends, while the legs of females are straight no matter what the insect's size.

Various uses were suggested for the males' lanky limbs: perhaps they helped them clamber through tree branches (the larvae develop in dead timber); maybe they were used for grasping the females, guarding them against other males by gripping them around the shoulders in a loving embrace. It turns out, however, that they use them for wrestling.

The aim of the largest males is to hook an opponent under the front armpit and fling him off the tree. This can be difficult because it brings the leg close to a competitor's small but powerful jaws. Damaged individuals missing antennal segments or leg portions are often found. Not all competitions end in combat. Males size each other up, head to head and leg to leg, and smaller males usually withdraw to leave the arena, and the female, to the victor. More evenly matched males move on to head butting. Only a few conflicts escalate into insect jujitsu. No wonder it took so long for entomologists to work out what such legs were used for.

Best wrestler

NAME **male harlequin beetle** *Acrocinus longimanus*
LOCATION   Mexico to Northern Argentina
ABILITY   uses its long front legs to flip over opponents

The word swarm most accurately applies to bees when they congregate in a seething mass around the queen or take to the air in a huge cloud. But it has also come to mean any large number of insects occurring and flying together. Without doubt the largest 'swarms' are of locusts, but calculating just how large is fraught with difficulty when they extend beyond the horizon in every direction.

Locust plagues have been known since antiquity, perhaps the most famous being the eighth of the ten plagues in the biblical Exodus. Until recently, most reports were anecdotal, simply referring to 'huge' (therefore uncountable) numbers. One account comes from 1784, when a swarm in South Africa covered an estimated 5,000 sq km (2,000 sq miles). The swarm was blown out to sea and washed up dead on the strandline, 1 metre (3 ft) high, for 80 km (50 miles). The stench of the rotting corpses was smelled 250 km (150 miles) away.

The best accurate guess we have for the largest swarm is from Kenya in 1954. Fifty locust clouds covering 1,000 sq km (400 sq miles) were observed from reconnaissance aircraft. They reached between 1 and 1.5 km (up to 1 mile) into the air and were estimated to contain 50 billion insects, weighing a total of 100,000 tonnes.

Locusts don't always congregate in destructive clouds. Normally they live in small numbers and hop about fairly harmlessly just like other grasshoppers. They use their green coloration to hide in the herbage and shun each other. But physical and chemical changes occur to their bodies if favourable feeding means that survival rates are high. If the young hoppers are frequently touched on the hind legs as they grow (because they are bumped into and kicked by their kindred), instead of growing into the long-legged, green solitary-phase adults, they develop into the short-legged, but long-winged, yellow and brown adults of the gregarious phase, and swarming may occur.

Largest swarm

NAME	**desert locust** *Schistocerca gregaria*
LOCATION	Africa
ATTRIBUTE	many millions of insects fly together

Longest-lived adult

NAME   **common black pavement ant** *Lasius niger*
LOCATION   North America, Europe, northern Asia
ATTRIBUTE   lived for nearly 29 years in a laboratory nest

Different animals have evolved various strategies to make sure they leave a significant contribution in the next generation. Large birds and mammals invest a great deal of time and energy producing small numbers of large embryos that they either incubate as eggs in the nest or inside the protective envelope of the womb. To ensure success, these creatures need to be large and long-lived so that, if they fail during one breeding season, they can try again the next.

Insects remain mostly small and usually lay large numbers of tiny eggs. The larvae grow quickly to produce new adults in an attempt to out-pace predators. Larvae of some species remain hidden and feed leisurely before becoming a short-lived adult. Others invest in small numbers of larvae already nearly mature when they are laid.

Queen ants, however, achieve longevity by creating a superorganism – the colony – around them. Each ant nest is created from scratch by a single founding queen. Already mated, she keeps a store of sperm for her entire life with which to fertilise her eggs. Mostly she produces workers, sterile females whose sole purpose is to build and protect the nest and forage for food to rear the grubs. The queen has only one task – to lay eggs. She does this in the nest, fed by her daughters, who take care of her every need.

Removed from the dangerous bug-eat-bug world outside, the queen can survive for many years. Quite how long, we are still guessing. The oldest on record is a queen of the black pavement ant, *Lasius niger*, which lived for nearly 29 years in the laboratory of German entomologist Hermann Appel.

Shortest larval stage

NAME **tsetse flies** in the genus *Glossina*

LOCATION sub-Saharan Africa

ATTRIBUTE larva pupates (becomes a chrysalis) immediately it is 'born'

A parent's investment in its offspring is one of the most important drives in biology. In insects, it determines where eggs are laid, how many or how few, how big they are, whether they are guarded, if the young hatchlings are tended and whether a provision of food is stored for them. The life cycle of virtually any insect can be distilled down to its eggs and their (hopefully successful) passage through larvahood.

It is during the larval portion of an insect's life that all the feeding and growing is done. This can be a lengthy process, especially if the foodstuff is relatively nutrient-poor, like rotten timber, or prey food items are scarce. The adults then mate, disperse and lay eggs, and in many species adult life is over in a few days or even hours. Tsetse flies break this mould.

About 30 species of tsetse flies, *Glossina* species, live in sub-Saharan Africa. The adult females are bloodsuckers and transmit sleeping sickness (trypanomiasis), a deadly microbial disease. It spreads in rather the same way as malaria in that protozoa (micro-organisms) are injected into human blood with the saliva of an infected tsetse fly.

The blood meal is important for the tsetse fly. Like the malaria mosquito, it needs blood protein to nourish its offspring. But whereas the mosquito divides its nutritional intake among hundreds of eggs, the tsetse concentrates it all on just one.

The single egg hatches into a larva in a uterus-like pouch inside the female fly's abdomen. The larva feeds there for about nine days on secretions from glands in the uterus (sometimes referred to as 'milk') so that when it is 'laid' into the soil it is fully grown and immediately pupates. The free-living larval stage lasts just a matter of minutes. The new adult emerges a month later.

The tsetse has taken a different reproductive strategy from the usual insect tactic of laying lots of eggs in the hope that at least some larvae get through to adulthood. By adopting an almost mammalian approach, and nurturing one 'baby' at a time, the fly significantly increases each offspring's chances. It can produce a new larva every nine days and itself may live for up to four years.

Best kicker

NAME   **wetas** in the families Anostostomatidae and Rhaphidophoridae
LOCATION   New Zealand
ATTRIBUTE   defensive kicks with spiny back legs

The wetas of New Zealand and the surrounding islands are textbook examples of radial evolution. One of the most isolated places on the planet, the New Zealand archipelago has been colonised, over millions of years, by a strange ragtag assortment of creatures. At some point, many millions of years ago, a pregnant female cricket-like creature was probably washed up on the shores aboard a floating log. It found a virgin land with no other crickets (or much else) to compete with, and with no terrestrial mammals – the main predators of crickets elsewhere in the world. It was set to flourish.

As its descendants spread through the many islands and land masses of this new world, these cricket-like animals adapted to new climates, new habitats, new ecological niches and different foodstuffs. Some still ran around on the ground; others climbed trees, burrowed in the soil or lived in caves. And over evolutionary time, isolated populations developed into new and separate species, especially on some of the outlying islands. Today there are thought to be about 70 different species.

With no mammalian predators from which to flee, wetas developed two of their most distinctive characteristics – large size (see page 92) and lack of wings. Even though they have no significant ground-dwelling predators, wetas still have to defend themselves against birds, other insects, lizards and frogs. They do this by kicking. Although lacking wings to rub them against, wetas have retained the large back legs so distinctive of grasshoppers, bush-crickets and their relatives. The trailing edges of the back legs are armed with stout spines. When the weta is threatened, it raises them above its head, presenting a prickly mace with which to clobber the head of its aggressor.

Unfortunately, the wetas were no match for the stowaway land mammals that arrived when humans colonised New Zealand. The Polynesian rat probably arrived with the Polynesians who founded the Maori civilisation around 1280 CE. The black and brown rats arrived with European settlers in the 17th and 18th centuries. We do not know how many weta species have become extinct since humans arrived, but today many species are endangered or declining.

Most organised society

NAME   **higher termites** in the family Termitidae
LOCATION   Africa, Asia and Australia
ATTRIBUTE   complex caste system with division of labour on an industrial scale

The 'social' insects (bees, wasps, ants and termites) live in large colonies. These are often housed in complex nests and they require co-ordinated foraging to feed themselves and the developing brood. To prevent chaos there must be some division of labour. So it is that builders build, foragers forage, soldiers fight, nursemaids care for the young and a queen lays eggs.

Among the largest, and most complex, of these colonies are the fungus-growing Old World termites. In a large termite nest, there may be 15 different sizes of insect. Some of these are different age stages. Unlike bees, wasps and ants, which have grub-like larvae, termite eggs hatch into nymphs, fully legged and capable of nest activities. As the nymphs grow they shed their skin at predetermined intervals, growing larger at each moult. But they do not all grow along the same growth pathway. There are different developmental careers, leading to differently sized and shaped individuals.

One developmental pathway leads to nymphs with wing buds. At each moult the buds, containing embryonic wings, grow larger until fully winged and sexually mature males and females (alates) make a mass emergence from the nest to mate and found new colonies. Another pathway leads to sterile 'neuter' nymphs, and this pathway divides to create several career paths. Soldiers have large, tough heads containing either powerful jaws or a snout (nasus) through which sticky defensive glue is squirted onto enemies. Small workers chew the leaf or wood fragments, and large workers carry them back to the fungus gardens inside the nest.

The final task of a termite may be determined in the egg. The queen produces a 'juvenile' hormone, effectively preventing sexually reproductive adulthood by inhibiting wing growth and the other body transformations that create alates. Elsewhere in the colony, pheromones (chemical scents) produced by the other individuals inhibit or recruit the various career paths.

Most unsavoury defecation behaviour

NAME **lily beetle** *Lilioceris lilii* and other species
LOCATION originally Eurasia, but now introduced worldwide
ATTRIBUTE bathes in its own faeces

Brightly coloured lilies are cultivated the world over for their beautiful blooms and shining foliage. But wherever they are grown, they are also attacked by annoying pests that skeletonise the leaves and shred the petals. Lily beetles, *Lilioceris lilii* and other species, have been accidentally transported around the world from their native range in Europe and Asia – also the native range of their food-plants, lilies and snake's-head fritillaries – and are irritating garden pests wherever they occur.

These beetles can appear to the frustrated gardener to be immune to insecticidal sprays, and they return undaunted after each chemical dousing. A major part of this resistance to pesticides is down to the unusual behaviour of the beetle larvae. Their defence has not evolved specifically as a response to humans armed with chemical poisons, but as protection against predation by their natural enemies.

Lily beetle larvae are smooth, shining slug-like creatures. As is usual for insect larvae, they have leaf-chewing mouthparts at the front end, but in a departure from normal animal structure, the anus is situated halfway along the ridge of their back. This enables them to cover themselves with their copious semi-liquid excrement. Most insects, like other animals, avoid contact with their own faeces, not just because there may be pathological disease organisms in it, but because they can become clogged and glued with the stuff. Lily beetle larvae, by contrast, positively wallow in theirs.

This unhygienic behaviour has two benefits against natural predators and parasitoids. It hides them under a blanket of random globules and lumps, which makes them difficult to detect, and it makes them unpleasant morsels, either to eat or to come into physical contact with. As a side-effect, it also acts as a protective coating that prevents many pesticide sprays from reaching the larva.

The scarlet lily beetle, *Lilioceris lilii*, is the commonest lily pest in temperate regions. A similar Eurasian species, which has red legs instead of black, is called *L. merdigera*. Its name means 'I carry dung'.

Life is short. Most insects are short-lived not because senility and decrepitude come early, but because they soon get caught and eaten by something bigger. An insect that dies of old age is a very rare beast. But no matter how short its life, if an organism can reproduce, its life cycle can still be successful and stable enough to create a self-perpetuating population.

There is one group of insects renowned for their short lives. The mayflies take their scientific name, Ephemeroptera, from the notion that they are ephemeral – that they last only a short time. Well known to fly-fishing anglers for their early-morning appearance over the water, but late-afternoon absence, they have given rise to the slight myth that they live only for a day.

Like most insects, they live much longer than this, but as a secretive, non-flying larva. It is during the one- or two-year larval stage that all the insect's feeding and growing is done. The adult insects have poorly formed, non-functional mouthparts, so the adults do not feed at all.

There are few genuine measures of brief insect lives, but the compact history of some mayflies has been well studied. Females of the American sandburrowing mayfly, *Dolania americana*, survive adulthood for about five minutes. During that time they must find and mate with males, then return to the water from which they emerged to lay eggs for the next generation.

Mayflies are unique among insects in that they have a winged and flying final larval stage, called a sub-adult by entomologists, or a dun (because of its dull brown colour) by anglers. This gives an individual mayfly some extra time to disperse or hide on nearby vegetation before the final moult to pale delicate adult occurs. But females of *Dolania* do not make that final change. They mate and lay eggs as duns, and they lack functional legs so cannot perch on waterside vegetation to rest a while. For them, adult life truly is very short.

Shortest-lived adult

NAME	**mayflies** in the order Ephemeroptera
LOCATION	worldwide
ATTRIBUTE	typical adult life of one species just five minutes

Most explosive insect

NAME   **bombardier beetles** in the genus *Brachinus* and other species

LOCATION   worldwide

ATTRIBUTE   internal chemical combustion to explosive effect

Insects are constantly under threat of attack from larger predators, and many of their strange structures and peculiar behaviours are adapted to enable them to escape from enemies or prevent harm. A common defence method is to exude some foul body fluid, either toxic haemolymph (insect blood), poisonous glandular oils or excrement (see page 184).

Bombardier beetles, however, use chemical warfare, and have developed their own explosive defence. Inside the abdominal tip are two sets of paired glands that generate and store, in separate reservoirs, the unstable chemicals hydrogen peroxide and hydroquinones. When needed, these chemicals are squeezed through one-way valves into a tough crucible reaction chamber just inside the anus. Here they mix with the catalytic enzymes catalase and peroxidase. A sudden high-temperature reaction takes place, producing irritating and noxious chemicals called p-benzoquinone. At 100°C (212°F), the chemicals take the form of a boiling gaseous spray.

The spray is powered by the release of oxygen gas from the hydrogen peroxide, which builds up intense pressure in the crucible, pushing the reactants out through the beetle's rear end with an audible pop. The insect gets its military-sounding name from this extraordinary artillery-like explosive behaviour.

The stinging chemical cloud is released into the face of any would-be attacker through a tight flexible nozzle, which can be aimed in almost any direction, including over the beetle's back and forwards beneath its legs. If it cannot point its vent at the precise point of attack, the beetle can bounce the hot chemical jet off two small reflector plates just behind the slit-like opening.

Bombardiers use their deterrent spray mostly against ants. In laboratory experiments, they have been shown to be able to aim the hot benzoquinone jet with superb precision at a leg or individual leg segment. In an ant assault, they shoot straight at the jaws biting whichever of their limbs (or other body part) is under attack. If one explosive spray is not enough, the beetles can eject up to 20 hot squirts, buying enough time to run or fly to safety.

Longest sperm

NAME   *Drosophila bifurca*

LOCATION   North America

ATTRIBUTE   sperm 20 times longer than the male that produces it

Throughout the animal kingdom, the usual sexual split is based on females producing small numbers of relatively large ova (eggs) and males producing prodigious quantities of tiny sperm. This has given rise to a conflict of interests between males and females, often called the battle of the sexes. It pays males (in terms of future offspring) to mate as often and with as many partners as possible, whereas the female's best interests are served by being genetically choosy in her mate to ensure the best offspring.

Typically, millions of minuscule sperm compete for each egg, so when entomologists discovered a group of insects that create only a few giant sperm, they were presented with a mystery to unravel. *Drosophila bifurca*, like others in its genus, is only 2–3 mm (0.1 in) long, but males produce sperm over 58 mm (2.3 in) long. Almost all of this length is the long whip-like tail, coiled up like a ball of string. For each egg produced by a female, the male produces only six sperm in what are also the largest testes, relative to body size, of any insect. How could

such an unusual and ungainly sex system have evolved?

The female genital tract is not just a calm passage through which the sperm gently swim. There are physical and chemical obstacles to ensure only the best sperm get through to have a chance of fertilising the eggs. In many organisms this may mean the strongest, fastest, or most enduring sperm get through.

In females of *Drosophila bifurca*, the reproductive tract is slightly longer than the huge sperm, and it is coiled like a giant, hollow spring in the female abdomen. Only the longest sperm get through.

How this evolutionary arms race (lengthening tract versus lengthening sperm) benefits the flies is not clear. It may be that only the best-nourished and most able males can generate the longest sperm, and that their fertilisation success is a reflection of their physical prowess, though it is a hidden measure which females are incapable of assessing even when mating is over.

Largest parasite

NAME   **batwigs (parasitic earwigs)** in the genera *Arixenia* and *Xeniaria*

LOCATION   Southeast Asia

ATTRIBUTE   large parasites on small bats

Almost all mammals and birds have parasites living in their nests, in their fur and feathers, or in their very flesh. Lice, fleas, flukes and mites are all relatively tiny, and nuisance though they may be, they rarely cause serious bother to their hosts. Even when they attack susceptible youngsters or sickly individuals, the host can usually carry on a more or less normal life.

But spare a thought for the naked cave bats of Southeast Asia, which have to contend with parasitic earwigs crawling over their diminutive bodies. Most earwig species are easily recognisable from their tail pincers, which are used menacingly if they are threatened, but which are mostly used to help fold the delicate flight wings under the short leathery wing cases. The batwigs, as they might be called, have tiny eyes, short non-functional tail forks and no wings. They live all their lives on the bodies, and in the roosts, of the virtually hairless cave bats, *Cheiromeles* species, of Indo-Malaysia and the Philippines.

These are small bats, under 145 mm (6 in) long, so a 20-mm (1 in) batwig clinging to its short body is rather like a lobster living on the back of a human being. On one occasion 12 were found on a single bat. The earwigs are not blood-suckers or flesh-eaters, as are most mammalian parasites. Instead they seem to feed on skin gland secretions, dead and peeling skin flakes, bat dung and dead insects. They actively scamper over the bats when their hosts are roosting, and have stout claws with large gripping pads to cling on during flight. Unlike many parasites, they readily leave their hosts to explore the cave roosts, but they are much more than mere nest scavengers. They have evolved precise and close links with the bats and each earwig species occurs only on one bat species.

Highest heat tolerance

NAME	**Sahara desert ant** *Cataglyphis bicolor*
LOCATION	North Africa (Sahara Desert)
ABILITY	forages in the blistering heat of the midday sun when all else shelters

Since they cannot control their own internal temperatures, insect bodies follow the temperature of their ambient surroundings. Cold slows down the mechanisms of gas exchange, nutrient metabolism, nerve impulses and muscle contraction, so physical movements slow down too. But they soon recover if the temperature goes back up. Heat is much more of a killer. Not only does it irreversibly damage proteins and other body chemicals by cooking them, it greatly increases water loss, leading to death by desiccation. So what is an ant doing out foraging during the very hottest part of the day in one of the hottest places on the planet?

Sahara desert ants, *Cataglyphis bicolor*, emerge from their burrows when the surface temperature reaches 56°C (133°F). They dash around for a few minutes before disappearing back down their burrows. Nothing else living is about.

The surface temperature may reach 60°C (140°F), but the body of the ant does not quite reach this dangerous temperature. It is a long-legged species, and by raising its body away from the ground a crucial 4 mm (0.2 in), the air through which it moves is 6–7°C (11–13°F) cooler than the sand. It also runs at about 1 m/s (3.28 ft/s), which is extremely fast for an insect and may help to cool it as the breeze rushes past. The core body temperature at which the ant dies is 55°C (131°F), so it does not have long on the surface before it must retreat.

These ants have evolved their foraging strategy for a very good reason. With nothing else on the surface, they have no competitors and no enemies. Fringe-toed lizards are the ants' main predators, but even these hardy animals hide from the sun at this time of day. And what do the ants find to eat? Dead insects, killed by the ferocious heat.

Most diverse life histories

NAME **scuttle flies (phorids)** in the family Phoridae

LOCATION worldwide

ATTRIBUTE greatest range of larval habits in any animal group

Scuttle flies are so named for their habit of running about, rather than flying off. They are small, 6 mm (0.2 in) at the longest and usually only 2 mm (0.08 in), stout, rather hunched, with short, rounded wings. There are over 3,000 known species, but they all look rather similar and are so poorly studied that even experts have trouble identifying and naming them. And yet, their life histories are more varied than any other comparable group of organisms.

Phorids are often called coffin flies because some species breed in carrion, and they have been discovered after passing through possibly hundreds of generations in deeply buried coffins exhumed several years later. Elsewhere they lay their eggs in other types of decaying organic matter, including: mammal, bird and insect dung; dead snails and insects; refuse in the nests of bees, wasps, ants and termites; rotting fungi and toadstools; dead leaves and damaged plant stems.

A few species have been found mining burrows inside leaves, although they may have been using a mine created by another insect. They have been found feeding on seeds, flowers, leaves, roots, ears of corn (maize) and fruits.

Some species seek out the well-protected, but nutritionally attractive food stores in bees' nests, where they lay their eggs so that their larvae can feed surreptitiously on the pollen and nectar collected by their hosts. Others infiltrate wasp nests, where their larvae steal the stock of dead spiders or insects kept for the wasp grubs.

A large number of scuttle flies are internal parasitoids (see page 38) of other insects (beetles, flies, aphids, cockroaches, bees, ants, wasps, termites, moths and grasshoppers) and of earthworms, snails, slugs, spiders, centipedes and millipedes. Frog eggs and wounds on humans and stock animals have also been used by the larvae of several species.

Elsewhere, phorid larvae have been found living in slime moulds, birds' nests and mole tunnels. If these natural habitats were not enough, phorids show their versatility in the most unusual of manmade situations too – a snake specimen preserved in alcohol, a beet pickled in vinegar, a tin of boot polish and a pot of blue paint have all been home to scuttle flies.

Most bizarre reverse metamorphosis

NAME   **batflies** in the family Streblidae

LOCATION   tropical America, Africa, Asia and Australia

ATTRIBUTE   adult turns into a maggot

Insect metamorphosis, the transition from larva (or nymph) to adult, is one of the wonders of nature. During the larval stage, all the eating and growing takes place, usually secretively or in some sheltered place, hidden away from danger. During adult life, there is a mobile (usually winged) phase, when mates can be located and dispersion to new egg-laying sites can occur. This life split has given insects a huge advantage over less adapted invertebrates and partly accounts for their unprecedented success on the Earth. It is not for batflies though.

Bats have their fair share of blood-sucking parasites, among them a strange series of flattened, hook-winged and long-legged creatures called batflies. One group, the family Streblidae, occurs only on bats, and they have made their relationship with their hosts deeply personal. When the adults hatch from the pupal case (chrysalis), on the floor of the cave or hollow tree below the bat roosts, they fly up to find each other and mate. The male dies soon after inseminating the female. The female then lands on a suitable bat victim, casts off her wings and legs, and burrows under the bat's skin. She then loses all features of the adult body plan (distinctly segmented head, thorax, abdomen) and becomes, in effect, a maggot.

Only the tip of her body, with breathing holes and genital opening, pokes out from the skin of the bat. She spends the rest of her life feeding on her host's blood fluids while nourishing her larvae, one at a time, within her own body, in an organ similar to the mammalian uterus. The larva is not released until it is nearly fully grown and, after falling to the ground beneath the bat roosts, pupates almost immediately. The normal process of insect metamorphosis is turned on its head.

Longest larval stage

NAME **golden jewel beetle** *Buprestis aurulenta*
LOCATION North America, but transported around the world
ABILITY to slow its development, staying a larva for
over 50 years

Most of a larva's time is spent eating and growing, but it eventually has to make a very important choice – when to change into an adult. For those with a short and easy life history, this choice is relatively straightforward: as soon as they are fully grown, larvae pupate and transform into adults. Larger insects, on the other hand, face a dilemma. They often need to feed and grow as larvae for several years, especially if they feed in dead wood, with its poor nutritional quality. The longer they take, the more dangers they will be exposed to: they are more likely to be discovered and eaten by predators, or succumb to a particularly cold winter. If they transform too soon, they may be weaker than those that waited, and they may not be able to compete successfully for territories, mates or egg-laying sites.

This leads to some insects spending highly variable times in the larval stage. An extreme example of this is the golden jewel beetle, *Buprestis aurulenta*. It lays its eggs on damaged, dead or dying conifer trees. The larvae bore down through the bark and into the heart wood where they feed, usually for 2–4 years, before emerging as adults. However, in every batch of eggs there are always some that take longer, often 15–20 years. It is as if the beetle is deliberately hedging its bets by having some fast- and some slow-growing larvae. The record (so far) is held by two larvae that were uncovered by sanding the timbers in a building in British Columbia, where they had been quietly nibbling away for 51 years. And still they were not fully grown.

Best jumper

NAME **spittle bug or froghopper** *Philaenus spumarius* *
LOCATION Europe, northern Asia, North America
ABILITY jumps 100 times its body length

Getting out of the way quickly is the typical insect response to attack or disturbance. This usually involves extending the wings and flying off, but for a few species, jumping proves to be a quicker and more effective method. Grasshoppers, fleas and click beetles are all experts in the field, but froghoppers (also called spittle bugs) are the champions.

These small, blunt-faced insects are more familiar in their larval form, when the sap-sucking nymphs generate the spittle of their name, by bubbling air through their liquid excrement to make the cuckoo spit that maligns cuckoos. The adult bugs are mottled greens and browns and seldom seen because they can flick away in the blink of an eye.

These small insects are only 6–7 mm (0.2–0.3 in) long, but can jump over 100 body lengths in a single bound. The leap has a take-off velocity of 4.7 m/s (16.9 kph, 10.5 mph) and within a thousandth of a second the insect reaches an acceleration force equivalent to 550 gravities (an astronaut in a rocket reaches only 5 gravities).

Froghoppers achieve these astonishing feats not by muscular force alone, but by storing an elastic energy and suddenly releasing it, just like a bow releasing an arrow. Over one-tenth of the insect's body weight is taken up by huge muscles in the hind portion of the thorax. These muscles, called trochanteral depressors, are attached to the trochanter, a segment at the base of the hind legs. The muscles pull for a few seconds, bending a stiff but flexible bow-shaped arch made of chitin (a hard but bendy material) and a rubber-like protein called resilin, inside the froghopper's thorax. At a critical tension, mechanical latches pressing together on the insect's legs ping open and the spring-power built up in the arch is released, suddenly propelling the legs down and out, and the insect forwards and up.

* **Stop Press** See page 288 for the latest news on this record.

Best dancer

NAME **fruit flies** in the family Tephritidae

LOCATION worldwide

ABILITY foot-fancy and wing-waving courtship dances without comparison

There is no point in mating with the wrong species. It is a waste of time and an exposure to potential danger. Offspring are unlikely, and would probably be sterile. Courtship is a series of visual, tactile, sound and chemical messages exchanged between potential mates to make sure they are making the right choice. In insects, where there are so many similar-looking species, courtships can be very complex.

The wings of fruit flies (family Tephritidae) are decorated with dots, flashes, bars and mottled lacy patterns. These 'picture wings' are waved about during the build-up to mating, and are an important part of the flies' courtship dances. A dance starts with two flies signalling to each other. Wing-waving allows the flies to judge the markings, which vary from species to species and sometimes between male and female. Most dancers face each other, and as one makes a move, the other responds. Legs are lifted up and put down, wings are waggled or vibrated at different angles, there are side-to-side and back-and-forth moves. There may be head touching, the antennae brushing each other. Mouthparts sometimes meet in a kiss to exchange body fluids.

Choosing the best dancer is not just to get a species match. It can also indicate a well-nourished, agile and alert partner, a profitable source of genetic input for offspring. The females can be very discerning, as has been found with the Mediterranean fruit fly, *Ceratitis capitata*, an agricultural pest. Huge sums are spent trying to control it with the mass release of artificially bred sterile males. Irradiating the males destroys the sperm, so all matings with wild females produce barren eggs. Unfortunately, sterile dancers prove less attractive to females, who can identify fertile males by their natural rhythm. However, giving the irradiated males aromatherapy with ginger root extract seems to make them better dancers, with increased sexual success.

Best thief

NAME   **cobweb beetle** *Ctesias serra*

LOCATION   Europe and northern Asia

ABILITY   steals the food from under the very noses of its spider hosts

To be a good thief is to take without the loss ever being noticed or the taker ever seen. There are many thieves in nature, from the casual scavenger finding the leftovers of another's meal, to the brood parasite that lays its eggs in the food store of another's nest. The takers are usually smaller than those from which they take, and have to be nimble, dashing in when they get the chance.

There is one thief, however, so confident that it lives permanently with its victims, taking whenever it feels like it, and leaving its host unaware of what is going on. Looking like an animated boot-brush, the bristly larva of a small black beetle, *Ctesias serra*, lives under the loose bark of old or dead trees. It crawls over the messy silk sheet-webs spun by the many spiders that inhabit this secret world.

The spiders emerge by night, making brief forays out onto the surface of the bark. They capture their prey by feeling for vibrations on their untidy webs made by beetles and other small invertebrates crawling through the narrow space under the peeling bark. They then pounce, kill it with their venom, wrap it and eat it at their leisure. Occasionally they must find their victims gone, because the *Ctesias* larvae feed on the spiders' food.

The larvae are immune to attack from the spiders. Their long, stiff bristles are fragile and easily break off, clogging the mouthparts of any spider foolish enough to bite. They also avoid detection by confusing the spiders. The larva has a tuft of very long stiff hairs at its tail-end, which it vibrates if it becomes disturbed. This sets up jamming vibrations across the silk strands so the spider cannot judge the direction or distance of the source.

Ctesias is very closely related to the museum beetle, *Anthrenus verbasci*, a major pest of stored skins and pelts. Before humans started collecting wildlife, the museum beetle scavenged in spiders' webs, birds' nests, and in the feathers and fur of old carrion.

Honeybees have become icons of busy hard work, constantly on the move, foraging, nest-building and generally keeping busy. In Aesop's fable it was the ants that were portrayed as hard-working. Their small size and agile antics suggest that insects are constantly on the move, but in reality these are just bursts of frantic activity between extended periods of hiding and shelter.

Mostly these periods of quiet are when roosting at night or during poor weather, but one group of insects takes stillness to an extreme and does not move for weeks or months. They are roused, not by a gentle change in the weather, gradually increasing day length or slow ticking of a biological clock. They are waiting for a particular event.

Fleas, master hoppers and nuisance bloodsuckers, live a life poised on the brink of one supreme risk. Can they find a host? Unlike lice, which never leave their hosts and live their entire life cycle in the fur or feathers of their victims, fleas follow the style of more 'advanced' insects, and their larvae live in a different habitat from the adults. Flea eggs, dropped willy-nilly, fall into the nest of the host animal. The worm-like larvae feed on the adult fleas' droppings (effectively dried host blood) that fall into the debris of the nest.

When fully developed, the larva spins a cocoon and transforms into an adult. Then it waits, very patiently. Because of the mobile nature of fleas' victims, there is no guarantee that a nest will be occupied when pupation is complete. If the flea emerges from its chrysalis too early, it may have a long wait for breakfast. Instead, it remains dormant until the right moment.

That moment is when a new blood-laden host walks past. The flea, fully complete in adult form but still resting in the pupa, is roused by the vibrations of passing footsteps. Within seconds it climbs out and springs onto its chosen victim to take the blood meal for which it has waited so long. Pet owners, away on holiday for weeks, can return to find a perplexing flea infestation climbing out of the carpet to greet them. It is not that the flea population has necessarily increased dramatically while they were away but that the sudden synchronised emergence of hundreds of patient adult fleas makes the problem suddenly more noticeable.

Most patient insect

NAME	**fleas** in the order Siphonaptera
LOCATION	worldwide
ABILITY	waiting in the pupa until the exact moment a new host walks by

Best sunbathing protection

NAME   **darter dragonflies** in the genus *Sympetrum*

LOCATION   tropics worldwide

ABILITY   thermoregulation by special perching behaviour

Insects are poikilothermic (often incorrectly called 'cold-blooded'), which means that they cannot regulate their internal body heat. If it is cold out there, they are cold, and if an insect is cold it is slow and sluggish, unable to move.

To warm up enough to fly, insects sunbathe, capturing the warmth of the sun's rays to raise their body temperature above a flight threshold. This they do on flowers, leaves, rocks, bare earth and tree trunks. Some butterflies angle their wings to reflect the sun's rays, focusing them onto the thorax and warming up the flight muscles.

Once warmed up, insects face the opposite problem – the danger of overheating. The most obvious escape from heat is to shelter in the shade. Unfortunately, leaving the sunshine also means leaving behind potential prey, future mates and hard-won territories. For dragonflies concentrated around narrow stream and pool margins, cooling off in the shade can mean losing valuable egg-laying sites.

Tropical darter dragonflies have a behavioural alternative to seeking the shadows – they make their sun-absorbing profile as small as possible. By adopting the 'obelisk' pose, pointing its tail directly up at the sun, the dragonfly minimises the heat it receives from the sun while at the same time remaining out in the open, keeping its vantage point by the water's edge.

Most widespread insect

NAME   **painted lady butterfly** *Cynthia cardui*
LOCATION   worldwide, except Australia and New Zealand
ATTRIBUTE   widest natural spread of any insect in the world

Most insects are adapted to live in a particular habitat, in a particular place in the world. By concentrating their efforts on exploiting a narrow ecological niche, they are better able to compete against invaders and provide a suitable site for their own offspring. Most insects are quite sedentary, and on emerging as an adult they usually lay their eggs where they have been living. If it was good enough for their own larvahood, it will be good for their larvae. Flying off somewhere else is fraught with danger: of being eaten, not finding a mate, or not finding a good egg-laying site.

The commonest insects are usually restricted to one major part of the planet or other, and the 'zoogeographical' zones of the world each have their own distinctive faunas. Insects from Europe and northern Asia (the Palaearctic region) seldom spread to Afrotropical or Indo-Malaysian zones. Similarly, few North American (Nearctic) species also live in the South American (Neotropic) zone.

Staying put is playing safe, but being adventurous can pay huge dividends. Virgin territory can be invaded, parasitoids and diseases left behind, and new colonies established.

Spreading out can prevent in-breeding, and multiple populations can recolonise each other if some local catastrophe wipes a species out from one area.

Many insects have been spread around the world by the activity of humans. Some of these are deliberately introduced, such as honeybees, *Apis mellifera*, which have been transported well beyond their Asian and European homelands to South Africa, Australasia and the Americas. Others, such as lice and fleas, have travelled as stowaways.

The painted lady butterfly, *Cynthia cardui*, has not needed mankind to help it across the globe. It has made ocean- and continent-crossing journeys all by itself, driven by a strong migratory urge that reappears every year. In Europe, the painted lady disappears from much of the north with the onset of winter. Each spring it reinvades from North Africa and the Mediterranean, spreading farther north with each of several successive generations. Similar powerful movements occur throughout the world, except in South America (where it is relatively rare), and Australia and New Zealand, which have, so far, remained beyond its reach.

Extreme

Impact

Most useful scientific research tool · Most painful sting · Most revered insect · Most boring insect · Most eaten by humans · Most (un)wanted · Best human aphrodisiac · Most confusing insect · Most sinister insect · Most misplaced insect · Oldest surviving insect specimen · Most bewitching insect · Most important averted plague · Most unusually represented in art · Most musical insect · Most helpful clean-up · Worst plague · Most unusual mode of range extension · Most embarrassing insect · Most dangerous insect · Most valuable service · Most diverse insect fauna · Most irritating insect · Most valuable insect product · Most medically useful insect · Most dermatologically useful insect · Most dramatic recovery from near-extinction · Most forensic insect · Worst infestation of a person · Best example of evolution in action · Most endangered species · Most destructive insect · Most diverse group · Rarest insect

Most useful scientific research tool

NAME **fruit fly** *Drosophila melanogaster*

LOCATION introduced worldwide

ATTRIBUTE helping to unravel the underlying mysteries of genetics, DNA, mutation and evolution

In 1900, Harvard University biology professor William Castle was looking for an animal for his embryology students to breed. He wanted something cheap and easy to keep, and with a fast generation time to fit tight academic schedules and research against the clock. He plumped for a small common garden and domestic insect – the fruit fly, *Drosophila melanogaster*. He easily reared 200 fruit flies in just two weeks in an old milk bottle with half an old banana and a few rotting grapes.

One of Castle's colleagues, zoology professor Thomas Hunt Morgan from Columbia University in New York City, had also been rearing the flies. One day in 1909, Morgan noticed something odd with one specimen: instead of the usual brick red, its eyes were pure white. Soon Morgan was breeding red-eyed and white-eyed strains and examining what happened when they interbred.

Drosophila has been at the forefront of research into all aspects of genetics ever since. White-eyed forms were followed by brown eyes, orange eyes, hunchbacks, short wings, curly wings, pale bodies, dark bodies, long legs, short legs. Every portion of the fly's anatomy could be selectively bred and altered in the same way that thousands of years of selective breeding had altered farm animals and domestic pets. *Drosophila* can develop from egg to adult in as little as seven days, so the process took weeks, not centuries.

Even more bizarre genetic variants appeared. In bithorax flies the wing-bearing part of the body was duplicated so the flies now had four wings instead of two. Antennapedia genes produced legs where the antennae ought to be on the head. Genes also appeared to control aspects of behaviour such as mating.

More importantly, *Drosophila* has been able to demonstrate how genes are controlled inside a living organism – how they turn on and off, how they manage metabolic processes, and how radiation or chemicals can induce mutation. Because of *Drosophila*, we now have a firm picture of what chromosomes and genes are, even down to the molecular level of the genetic material in every living thing – the DNA.

Bees, wasps and ants have stings. They use these dangerous weapons to attack and kill (or sometimes just paralyse) prey, fight with each other, or defend themselves and their nests. Among this group of insects, all descended from a wasp-like stinging ancestor over 100 million years ago, are several pretenders to the title of worst sting. The issue was undecided until American entomologist Justin Orville Schmidt set about subjecting himself to as many stinging insects as he could get his hands on.

Using a four-point scale he contrived the Schmidt sting pain index, first published in 1984, with almost gleeful detail. At 1.0, the lowest sting pain value, were the sweat bees, whose attack was like a tiny spark had singed a single hair on your arm. The European hornet (*Vespa crabro*) came in alongside the honeybee at a mediocre 2.0 – like a matchhead that flips off and burns your skin. Top of the danger list was the bullet ant, *Paraponera clavata*, which scored 4.0+. Schmidt described the bullet ant's sting as like walking over flaming charcoal with a 3-inch rusty nail in your heel.

Bee, wasp and ant stings are adapted from parts of the egg-laying apparatus, which means that only females sting. A pair of venom-secreting glands drain into a poison reservoir attached to the hollow hypodermic sting shaft at the tip of the abdomen. Males do not sting, but the vast majority of these insects – the queens and the workers – are female.

Many ants no longer have functional stings. Instead they spray the contents of the poison sac through a small hole at the tip of the abdomen. The main constituent of ant venom is formic acid, which is similar to acetic acid, found in vinegar. *Paraponera* also produces a substance called poneratoxin, which induces slow, long-lasting contractions in mammalian muscle and blocks nerve channels. It is being studied for possible medical applications.

Most painful sting

NAME	**bullet ant** *Paraponera clavata*
LOCATION	Nicaragua to Paraguay
ATTRIBUTE	the most painful sting of any insect

Most revered insect

From at least 3000 BCE, scarab beetles were central to the religious beliefs of the Egyptians, and representations of them were common. Scarabs are large, impressive insects, but what captured the ancients' imagination was their behaviour, for most scarabs are dung beetles. The beetles first make a large ball of dung from the main pile. Next, walking backwards on their front legs they use the back pairs of legs to control and manipulate the ball of dung and roll it many metres away. Now they bury it deep in the soil and lay their eggs underground. When the eggs hatch, the grubs have a personal hidden food store, well away from the many other dung-feeding competitors.

The Egyptians took scarabs to be a symbol of the sun god Ra, the assumption being that the dung ball represented the sun being rolled across the sky. Scarabs were also used as a symbol for Cheper, the god of creation. This may be linked to the seemingly mysterious emergence of adult beetles up through the ground from their larval dung vaults.

A fabulous gold breast ornament, found in the tomb of Tutankhamun, shows a large black scarab pushing a red solar disc, its extended wings decorated with coloured glass and semi-precious stones. Elsewhere scarab shapes were roughly carved from simple stones. They have been found throughout the Mediterranean. Although many sources name the single beetle species *Scarabaeus sacer* as the original, at least five scarab genera have now been identified as models for known carved variants.

NAME **sacred scarabs of the ancient Egyptians**
various species of the family Scarabaeidae
LOCATION found worldwide, but their worship was
centred around the eastern Mediterranean
ATTRIBUTE most widely worshiped and respected insect

Most boring insect

NAME **death-watch beetle** *Xestobium rufovillosum*

LOCATION worldwide

ABILITY most insidious destruction of old timber-framed buildings

Imagine the deathbed scene: a darkened room; the shallow, barely audible, breaths of the dying person; the hushed family gathered around to watch. Suddenly the near silence is broken by the sound of tapping coming from the roof above, or perhaps from the very timber of the building. Although quiet, it is sharp and regular – like the ticking of the clock of life running out. Sinister though this may sound, the ticking has no connection to the death unfolding, more to the hush of the watchers present. Before our modern sanitisation of death in hospitals and hospices, in an age of timber-framed buildings, such a scene would be commonplace, and so too would be the wood-boring beetle making the taps.

The death-watch beetle is one of the largest of the woodworms, with a body length of about 7.5 mm (0.3 in). Its grubs are also large, and the damage the beetle does to wooden timbers can be great. This damage is compounded by the beetle's secrecy. It does not leave obvious bore-holes or heaps of dust, but tends to remain inside the timber, creating ever larger burrows, which combine to form voids. It is these voids that will eventually reduce the load-bearing strength of the beams to the point of breaking.

The death-watch is brought into the building as it is constructed, already living inside the huge oak, elm, beech or other hardwood joists and beams. Consequently it is only found in large, old wood-framed buildings, where monitoring is difficult and eradication is almost impossible. The tapping is made by the adult beetles, which grip the wood and bang their heads to sound their presence and find their way to potential mates in the interior darkness of the timber.

Forget witchetty grubs, bogong moth caterpillars or honeyed locusts on a stick, because although they are probably all very nutritious and good sources of protein, only a tiny proportion of the human population has ever eaten them. Instead, think of a tiny aphid-like creature from South and Central America – the cochineal insect, *Dactylopius coccus*.

Dactylopius coccus is found in the high, arid parts of Mexico and South America, where it feeds on prickly pear cactuses, *Opuntia ficus-indica* and other species. These minute insects, just 2–5 mm (0.1–0.2 in) long, live in large colonies and coat the cactuses with fluffy white waxy secretions. These are made by the wingless females, which spend all their time sucking out cactus sap. The soft waxy strands act as a defence, clogging up the mouthparts of potential predators if they try to attack. The males, by contrast, look like winged aphids.

As they suck out the plant fluids, the cochineal females produce large quantities of a deep-crimson pigment – a substance called carminic acid – which they store in their bodies. This complex biochemical is bitter to the taste and is another protection against being eaten.

Since Aztec and Maya times, cochineal has been used to colour cloth, cosmetics and foodstuffs, and the dried insects have been important goods for trade since at least 2200 BCE. After the Spanish conquest of Mexico (1519–21), cochineal was shipped to Europe and later to the rest of the world, and by 1600 it was second only to silver in its export value.

By the 19th century, chemical dyes, which were easily synthesised in industrial mills, had replaced labour-intensive 'natural' colours, such as cochineal. However, in a world that is turning away from artificial colours and flavours, original cochineal is regaining commercial viability, labelled as carminic acid, CI 75470, E120 or natural red 4. It will not, however, be labelled as suitable for vegetarians.

Most eaten by humans

NAME	**cochineal** *Dactylopius coccus*
LOCATION	Central and South America, introduced to Spain, North Africa and Australia
ATTRIBUTE	eaten by more people than any other insect

Most (un)wanted

NAME **Colorado beetle** *Leptinotarsa decimlineata*
LOCATION North America, transported to Europe and Asia by humans
ATTRIBUTE features in 'wanted' posters in police stations

In 1811, British-born traveller and naturalist Thomas Nuttall (1786–1859) was collecting specimens in the Rocky Mountains when he came upon a striking black and yellow striped beetle feeding on buffalo-bur, *Solanum rostratum*, a member of the nightshade family. Eventually the specimen came before American entomologist Thomas Say (1787–1834) who, in 1824, named it *Leptinotarsa decimlineata* after the ten black stripes down its back.

It might have remained a pretty, but rather insignificant, insect had it not, in 1859, been found destroying potatoes (the closely related *Solanum tuberosum*) in Nebraska hundreds of miles east of the Rockies. This was the start of a rapid spread eastwards, and by the time the beetle reached the Atlantic coast, in 1874, it was already a notorious agricultural pest. Originally called the ten-lined potato beetle, its rather spurious association with Colorado was made in 1867 when a small booklet warning of its devastations was published. The name stuck.

Potatoes were one of the staple foods of the northern hemisphere, and the beetle's arrival in Europe in 1877 was met with dismay. It was discovered in a small plot of about 5 hectares (12 acres) at Mülheim, in Germany. The plot was cordoned off, and the whole area was doused with petrol and burned. The Colorado beetle was eradicated in Europe, but it was only a matter of time before it would come back. Around this time, 'wanted' posters started to appear in ports, police stations and post offices around Europe. The posters showed illustrations of the brightly coloured beetles and their equally brightly coloured larvae devouring potato leaves.

Unfortunately, quarantine procedures were relaxed when Europe descended into war between 1914 and 1918. The next invasion of Colorado beetles was discovered in Bordeaux in 1922, and was widely blamed on the vast import of goods and materials that came with the US troops who had arrived in Europe in 1917. The beetle spread inexorably through Central Europe into Asia.

Today the beetle is still a regulated pest in the UK, Republic of Ireland, Sweden, Finland, Balearic Islands, Cyprus and Malta. To date these states are all free of Colorado beetles, and 'wanted' posters are still pinned up in ports and police stations.

In Marseille, in southern France, in 1772, the Marquis de Sade was accused of poisoning prostitutes with a concoction containing Spanish fly. There were no fatalities, but such was the seriousness of the crime that he was sentenced to death in his absence after he had fled to Italy. Since the time of the ancient Greeks and Romans, the supposed aphrodisiac effects of Spanish fly have been well documented, but so too has the dangerous nature of its poison.

Spanish fly is a beetle, *Lytta vesicatoria*, and with its brilliant metallic green body it is one of the more striking of the Meloidae, a family of beetles known as oil beetles because of the oily secretions they give off if touched or disturbed. This oil contains a powerful chemical called cantharidin, which is stored in the beetle's haemolymph (the insect equivalent of blood) and in the accessory glands around its sex organs.

If ingested, cantharidin is highly stimulating on the urinary tract, causing a tingling sensation and, in men, a prolonged erection. However, its erotic effects are overwhelmed by the serious medical disorders it also creates. These include cystitis, passing blood in the urine, and a powerful urge but inability to urinate. As the poison moves around the body, it creates respiratory difficulties, convulsions, gastroenteritis, confusion and can lead to death. The adult human fatal dose is about 0.03 g (0.001 oz), easily supplied by a single beetle.

The deadly nature of cantharidin was often exploited in ancient times as a means of execution. Instead of the poisonous hemlock cup, the condemned was given a draught of wine containing ground oil beetles. Grazing animal deaths are sometimes attributed to the beetles being eaten accidentally, in which case the meat is also poisonous.

The effect of cantharidin can easily be seen on the skin if an oil beetle is incautiously handled. A redness appears within minutes and later pustules arise which combine into a single large, fluid-filled blister, earning the insects the alternative name blister beetles. At one time blistering was a regular medical practice, to let out 'malignant humours', which were thought to have accumulated in the body. Cantharidin is still used in some parts of the world to dissolve warts.

Best human aphrodisiac

NAME **Spanish fly** *Lytta vesicatoria*
LOCATION Europe
ATTRIBUTE contains a chemical used as a love potion – and a poison

Most confusing insect

NAME   **ant-nest flies** in the genus *Microdon*

LOCATION   worldwide

ABILITY   to confound naturalists

In 1924 the Spanish naturalist Alejandro Torres Minguez described *Buchanania reticulata*, a new 'naked snail' from the Coma de l'Orri area in the Pyrenees. He had fallen into the same trap as a series of illustrious predecessors. The strange slug-like creature, with its reticulated skin, was in reality the bizarre larva of a hoverfly, *Microdon*.

It was at least the fourth time that this peculiar insect had been described as a mollusc. In Brazil in 1824, the German explorer Johann Baptist von Spix named it *Parmula cocciformis*, because of its resemblance to *Coccus* scale insects. The following year German naturalist Carl von Heyden called it *Scutelligera* (meaning 'shield-carrying') *ammerlandia*. And in 1907 another German zoologist, Heinrich Simroth, coined *Ceratoconcha* (meaning 'horned shell') *schulzei*. They had all been completely confounded by the creature's domed, legless and unsegmented body.

The confusion of the naturalists is completely understandable given the *Microdon* larva's peculiar form and odd life history. The adult fly (which is rather squat, with relatively short wings, but nevertheless very typically fly-like) lays its eggs in ants' nests, where the maggots feed on detritus in the colony and on the ant grubs. The flanged limpet-like shape of a *Microdon* larva is perfectly adapted for clamping down onto the ground, preventing any ants from getting a grip with their jaws.

The larva moves slowly, so as not to draw attention to itself, but left to its own devices in the brood chamber it can soon ripple over an ant larva, puncture it with its sharp mouthparts and suck out the body contents before discarding the empty shell. One *Microdon* larva can browse its way through 10 ant grubs in 30 minutes.

It was always assumed that *Microdon* was protected from the ants by its hard shell, but if one is transferred to another ant nest, the new ants try to attack it. This suggests that it is giving off some sort of chemical scent to fool its hosts. So it is not just human observers that are confused by *Microdon* larvae.

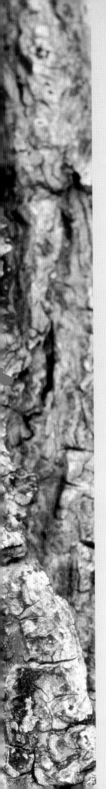

Most sinister insect

NAME   **death's head hawkmoth** *Acherontia atropos*

LOCATION   Mediterranean and Middle East

ATTRIBUTE   carries the sign of death, the skull, on its back

To a human, the death's head hawkmoth seems aptly named. The yellow skull-shaped mark on the back of its thorax has hollow eye sockets and narrow cheeks, and the moth, a widespread species from the Middle East and Mediterranean Europe, has long been shunned as a portent of doom. But what is the real purpose of its sinister-looking marking?

Hawkmoths fly at night or at dusk, when they risk the attention of bats but avoid the depredation of birds. During the day they hide, and most select a quiet spot on a dead leaf, tree branch or rock to roost. Blending in to the background will keep the moth out of harm's way most of the time. By folding its wings tent-like over its body it presents only its mottled front wings, which are camouflaged with sombre scales. The yellow thorax mark also helps to break up the outline of its dark body.

Nevertheless, many will still be stumbled upon, quite literally, by predators. If this happens, the moth suddenly flicks out its bright yellow hind wings. This startle response is heightened by the yellow thorax mark with its two dark eye spots. Like a face suddenly opening its eyes, the effect is very disconcerting.

If the moth's markings are startling, or sinister, its behaviour around humans is also very striking. Unlike many nectar-feeding moths, which have long, coiled tongues, the death's head hawkmoth has a short, stout tongue, perfect for sucking up honey. Where beekeepers use skep hives made from a woven basket, the hawkmoth is a regular intruder. If removed by the beekeeper, it can make an eerie whistling sound by expelling air through the same short, stout proboscis.

London apothecary James Petiver (1663–1718) is credited with coining the first English names for many British butterflies. Before him, long rambling Latin names were the order of the day. A few of Petiver's names are still used (Brimstone, for the bright yellow *Gonepteryx rhamni*), some have changed but are still recognisable (golden brown double streak is now brown hairstreak, *Thecla betulae*), but one stands out as the most intriguing of the lot.

In a list of newly acquired specimens, published between 1702 and 1706, he cites 'Papilio oculatus Hamspstediensis ex aureo fuscus – Albin's Hampstead Eye. Where it was caught by this curious person, and is the only one I have yet seen.' Petiver subsequently published a picture of it on a plate of 'eye-winge'd butterflies' in his famous book of British butterflies, *Papilionum Britanniae icones*, published in 1717. The person in question, Eleazar Albin (1690-1742), was certainly fuelled by curiosity. He published two major works: *Natural history of English insects* in 1720, and *Natural history of spiders and other curious insects* in 1736. But with his Hampstead eye butterfly, Albin put a spanner in the works that would not be cleared up for nearly 200 years.

For the next two centuries, Albin's Hampstead eye, later formalised by the 'modern' scientific names *Cynthia hampstediensis* or *Hipparchia hampstediensis*, was paraded through academic literature alongside all the other British butterflies. But in every single publication there was a caveat along the lines of 'not seen since Petiver's time'.

It was not until the end of the 19th century that the mystery of the curious Albin's curious insect was finally solved. Albin's original specimen resurfaced in London's Natural History Museum. It was, as many had suspected, an exotic – the meadow argus, *Junonia villida*. Its natural range is through Australia, New Zealand, Papua New Guinea, Samoa, Solomon Islands and New Hebrides. There is no way that Albin could have captured a live *Junonia* on Hampstead Heath. He had somehow mislabelled his specimens, to the detriment of scientific entomology for nearly two centuries.

Most misplaced insect

NAME **Albin's Hampstead eye** *Junonia villida*
LOCATION 18th-century London (allegedly)
ATTRIBUTE intrigued and confused naturalists for 200 years before its true origin was discovered

Oldest surviving insect specimens

NAME **Leonard Plukenet's collection**

LOCATION Natural History Museum, London

ATTRIBUTE has survived over 300 years of rough handling by curators, and attacks from mould, mildew and 'museum' beetles

Except in rare fossils, which have been randomly and accidentally preserved by the forces of nature, dead insects soon disintegrate. They are quickly scavenged by other small animals or rot away through the decaying effects of fungi and bacteria. And yet, for their size, insects are relatively easy to preserve in a museum. Simply dry them and they should last for many years. But how many years?

Until recently, quality was the sole aim of museum curators. When a bigger or better specimen came along, the old tatty one was binned. Before modern air-tight cabinets, specimens were constantly ravaged by mould or the larvae of *Anthrenus verbasci*, the 'museum' beetle. Whole collections were thrown out or destroyed according to the whims of the museum's governors or the fashions of the time, and it is only in the last 50 years that the importance of historical collections has been fully recognized.

London's Natural History Museum was founded as part of the British Museum, which first opened in 1759, and despite centuries of change it still has a few of the original specimens gathered by its founder, the physician, naturalist and collector Sir Hans Sloane. Among these are some of the oldest insect specimens still in existence. Most are butterflies.

James Petiver (1663–1718), apothecary and entomologist, preserved butterflies between two thin sheets of mica, sealed at the edges with gummed paper and housed in wooden boxes, much like magic lantern slides. The oldest of these dates from about 1702. Adam Buddle (1660–1715) was a botanist (the flowering bush buddleja is named after him) and in volume 12 of his leather-bound herbarium, in which grasses, sedges and rushes are pasted onto the pages, are interspersed many butterflies, also glued down onto paper. They are damaged, smudged and in poor condition, but 31 species are still recognisable. They were collected from around London between 1699 and 1715.

The oldest, though, are the 1,700 insect specimens, of various groups, pasted into a similar leather-bound tome by physician and naturalist Leonard Plukenet (1642–1706) and which passed to Sloane on Plukenet's death. A catalogue in Plukenet's hand gives details of these insects, which were originally collected in 1696 and 1697, mostly around London and Westminster.

Incidentally, the oldest pinned insect specimen is claimed by the Oxford University Museum of Natural History, which has a Bath white butterfly, *Pontia daplidice*, collected in 1702.

What's in a name? Most insects, if they have a common title at all, are named after their colour (for example, the clouded yellow or sulphur butterflies), their shape (stick insects or leaf bugs), where they live (water beetles or mountain ringlet), their behaviour (leaf-cutter ants or honeybees), or the damage they do (cabbage whites or woodworm). Butterflies and moths, prettily patterned and sometimes strikingly marked, offer a fascinating variety of names, such as death's head (see page 232), tiger moth (orange-striped), emerald (green), angle-shades (art deco), yellow underwing (self-explanatory) and silver Y (white mark in that shape). But the most unusual name comes from a 16th-century Yorkshire witch, the Mother Shipton.

Born around 1488, Ursula Southeil (or Sontheil) acquired a name for herself as a soothsayer and prophetess. Quite what she prophesied, and for whom, is now rather lost in myth and folklore. The first published account did not appear until 1641, 80 years after her death in 1561. Later biographers fabricated details of her life, and many of her most famous prophesies (carriages without horses, underwater men shall walk, iron in the water shall float) were 19th-century inventions. The only 'fact' that runs through most histories is that she married a carpenter, Toby Shipton, around 1512.

By the end of the 17th century, fact mattered little. By now Mother Shipton had become the perfect caricature for any witch story, often depicted as a wizened ugly hag. A small day-flying moth now carries her name. The moth is daintily marked, but close examination shows that the forewings are patterned with the grotesque outline of a twisted human head. It has a large hooked nose, pointed chin, toothless grin and small dark eyes – the face of Ursula Shipton peering out at the world.

Most bewitching insect

NAME	**Mother Shipton moth** *Callistege mi*
LOCATION	UK (also Europe and northern Asia)
ATTRIBUTE	British name commemorates a 16th-century soothsayer, prophetess and witch

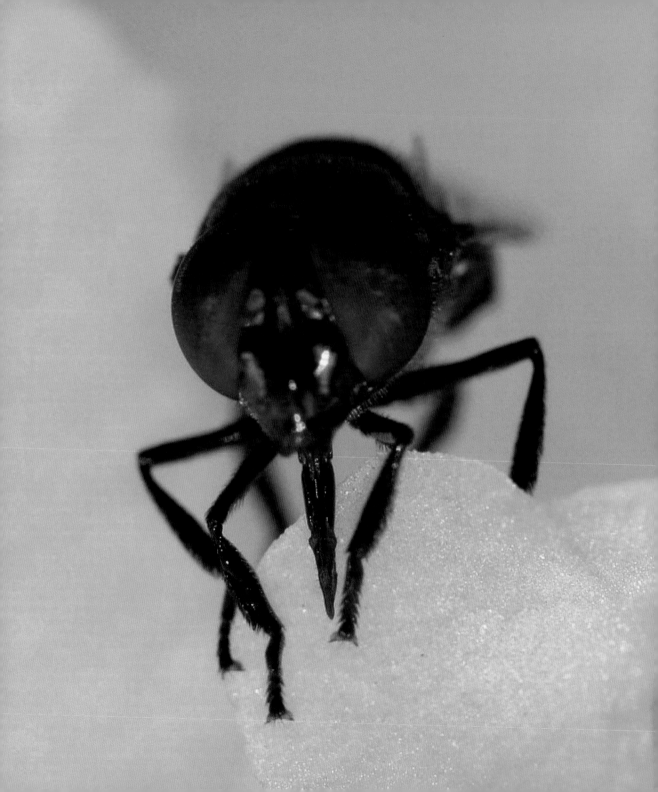

In 1988, maggots were reported to be infesting the wounds that livestock get by scratching themselves against fences, barbed-wire or thorn bushes. Ordinarily, very little would have been made of this report, except that these were larvae of the New World screw-worm fly, *Cochliomyia hominivorax*, from Central America, and they were discovered in Libya, the first time this insect had been found outside of its homeland.

Called a screw-worm because of the maggots' ability to screw themselves deep into exposed flesh, feeding on blood, pus and body fluids, this insect had long been known south of Mexico as a pest of wild and farm animals. It is not above attacking humans either – *hominivorax* means 'human-eating'. Noxious though it may be, it is a natural part of the local ecology, with its own predators and parasites, and native animals have built up resistance to it. Introduced to another continent, it was likely to wreak ecological havoc. By the end of 1988, the flies, each of which can lay up to 3,000 eggs, were known to have infested an area of 26,000 sq km (10,000 sq miles) where 2.7 million sheep, goats and cattle were grazing.

The United Nations embarked on an international project to avert a plague of biblical proportions. Millions of screw-worm flies were reared in carefully controlled secure environments in Mexico and the USA. Just after the adult flies emerged from their pupae, they were irradiated with a dose of radioactive caesium 137. This was not enough to injure them, but enough to make all the males sterile.

From December 1990 to October 1991 nearly 1.3 billion sterile flies were dropped in cardboard boxes from low-flying planes over the Libyan countryside. This 'sterile insect technique' works by swamping the area with useless sperm. The vast majority of fertile females, which mate only once, will find the irradiated sterile males, so their eggs will never hatch. Since then, *Cochliomyia hominivorax* has not been found in Africa again.

Most important averted plague

NAME   **New World screw-worm** *Cochliomyia hominivorax*
LOCATION   Libya
ATTRIBUTE   nearly caused grave human and animal suffering

Most unusually represented in art

NAME **European stag beetle** *Lucanus cervus*

LOCATION Europe

ATTRIBUTE achieved iconic status in medieval art despite its menacing form

Stag beetles are monstrous-looking creatures – large, dark, powerful and menacing. The huge jaws of the males can be a frightening sight, and folklore has blamed them for bad luck, inducing lightning and even carrying burning coals from the hearth to start house fires. Yet in medieval times the Christian Church, and the artists that decorated its places of worship, adopted the stag beetle as a most unusual icon. It achieved this status due to the obvious resemblance of its huge jaws to the antlers of deer. Deer were supposed to be able to fight snakes. In early Christian paintings, deer (especially well-antlered stags) were used to symbolise Christ, and often represented victory over some evil or other.

The first apparent (or at least earliest surviving) use of a stag beetle in this way is in an illuminated manuscript by Giovannino de Grassi, commissioned by Gian Galeazzo, Duke of Milan, in 1370. It shows a stylised horned beetle flying up towards God, surrounded by hermits as dictated by the religious feelings of the day, with similarly horned stags resting on the hillside below.

Other famous cameo roles for the stag beetle can be seen in Germany. Above the altar of the City Patron in Cologne Cathedral, it features in *Adoration of the Magi*, painted by Stefan Lochner between 1440 and 1445, and is also found in *Jesus' Prayer in the Garden of Olives*, the altar piece of the St Marien Church of Zwickau, in Sachsen, painted by Michael Wolgemut in 1479. Although often small and sketchy, the stag beetle is clearly visible in these and similar artworks.

One of the highest achievements of the beetle was to feature in several pictures by the great German artist Albrecht Dürer, whose *The Virgin Among a Multitude of Animals* (1503) and *Adoration of the Magi* (1504) show an anatomically very precise *Lucanus* scuttling across the foreground. Dürer was obviously fond of the beetle and his beautiful portrait of it (right), painted in 1505, marks a watershed in European art between sketchily stylised insect depictions and naturalistic pictures. His image, much copied by contemporary and later artists, would not look out of place in a modern identification guide.

1505.

Most musical insect

NAME **crickets** in the family Gryllidae, and **bush-crickets** in the family Tettigoniidae
LOCATION different species worldwide, but especially China and Japan
ABILITY to sing so melodiously that they are caged for human entertainment

For at least 2,500 years, small hopping insects have been caged by humans to entertain them. Crickets and bush-crickets sing to each other. It's a predominantly male pastime, since the males spend most of their time trying to serenade females or frighten off other males from their territory. They 'sing' by rubbing their raised front wings together.

On the underside of the cricket's right wing, one of the stiff wing veins is covered with a row of tiny pegs, which together form a long, comb-like file. On the upper surface of the left wing another vein is stiffened and raised into a scraper (plectrum). In bush-crickets (also called katydids) this arrangement is reversed – file on left wing, scraper on right. As the wings rub together, right over left (or left over right in bush-crickets), the plectrum plucks the series of pegs, causing the wings to vibrate at a frequency determined by the number and size of the pegs and the speed at which the wings move. This is rather like the thimbled fingers of a skiffle player 'drumming' on a washboard.

Two large areas of the wings, called the harp (because of its shape) and the mirror (because of its smoothness) act as amplifiers, elevating the scraping (called stridulation) to a level that can be heard over hundreds of metres. Each species has its own sound, variously described as chirps, trills, whirring, ticking, warbling and purring. The vibrations are usually in the range of 1,500 to 10,000 Hz (cycles per second), well within the range of human hearing (20 to 16,000 Hz), and many sound musical and melodious to us.

Since at least 500 BCE, the Chinese, Japanese and Koreans have kept crickets in small wire cages, woven bamboo baskets or perforated gourds, and taken them indoors to enjoy their music. As with all music, taste is highly personal, so it is impossible to pick out the most musical. Over 30 species were regularly kept and given suitably melodic-sounding names like golden bell (*Svistella bifasciata*), singing brother (*Gampsocleis gratiosa*) and weaving lady (*Mecopoda elongata*).

Most helpful clean-up

NAME	**cactus moth** *Cactoblastis cactorum*
LOCATION	eastern Australia
ATTRIBUTE	cleared Australia of its most invasive pest plant

In the 19th century, Australia was seen by the British as a virgin country, as the aboriginal people who already lived there were brutally pushed to one side. Many basic raw materials, from sugar to wool, began to be cultivated in the continent. One of these fledgling industries, cochineal production (see page 225), required the introduction of prickly pear cactuses (*Opuntia* species) on which these tiny insects would feed. With the advent of chemical dyes, cochineal farming soon waned, but the cactus was not to know this.

By 1900, several species of prickly pear cactus, notably *Opuntia inermis* and *O. stricta*, had been introduced from Central and South America. They thrived, especially in the subtropical climates of Queensland and New South Wales, and were soon out of control. Twenty-four million hectares (60 million acres) – an area the size of the United Kingdom – in eastern Australia had been infested. Half the infested area was now useless for agriculture. Possible biological control agents were sought back in the cactuses' original homelands. About 50 insect species that normally fed on *Opuntia* were shipped to Australia in quarantine to test their suitability.

Eventually 12 insect species were released to control prickly pear. The most important was a small, mottled grey and brown moth, *Cactoblastis cactorum*. The first releases were made in 1926, and they continued to 1932. By that time the cactuses had been all but destroyed by the moth's pink and black caterpillars, and during monitoring from 1932 to 1935 they were successfully keeping the cactus regrowth in check too. *Opuntia* is now no longer a problem plant in Australia.

Worst plague

NAME **bush fly** *Musca vetustissima*

LOCATION Australia

ATTRIBUTE part of a manmade ecological disaster only recently controlled

According to the Book of Exodus (chapters 7–12), of the ten calamities that fell upon Egypt when the Pharaoh refused to let Moses take the Israelites out of servitude, three were plagues of insects: lice (or gnats), flies and locusts. These noisome and noxious insects continue to plague humans today. Lice can be controlled by grooming. Locusts eventually eat themselves to starvation. Flies, on the other hand, are encouraged by human activities – and nowhere was this more dramatically demonstrated than in Australia in the late 19th and early 20th centuries.

European colonisation of Australia at the end of the 18th century brought a host of alien plants and animals as settlers tried to recreate the environments of their homelands in the northern hemisphere. The greatest environmental effect they had was to introduce an agriculture based on arable farming and grazing stock animals. The animals, mainly cows, were able to eat Australian plants, but the copious liquid dung they dropped was not at all to the taste of the native dung beetles, which were adapted to the hard, dry pellets of marsupials. It took just 11 cattle to remove 1 hectare (2.5 acres) of meadowland out of production each year, as it was slowly smothered with pats of unrecyled dung. Although beetles refused the dung, the bush fly *Musca vetustissima* quickly adopted it as food for its maggots, and what had been simply a nuisance turned into a plague of biblical proportions.

Late 19th-century travellers reported that great clouds of flies infested the air. It was impossible to breathe without swallowing them. The combination of stifling clouds of flies and pasture-loss prompted the Australian government to act, and since 1965 over 50 species of non-native dung beetles have been introduced from Africa, Asia and Europe. At least 20 of these are still thriving and expanding their range across Australia, and they have reduced bush fly numbers to acceptable, if still annoying, levels.

Most unusual mode of range extension

NAME   **Asian 'tiger' mosquito** *Aedes albopictus*
LOCATION   spreading around the world
ATTRIBUTE   transported around the world in secondhand tyres

Mosquitoes breed in stagnant water, where their larvae feed on micro-organisms and decaying organic matter. Although only a minor nuisance in cooler temperate zones, in the tropics their blood-sucking habits transmit many horrible diseases, including malaria, filariasis (minute worms in the blood), encephalitis and yellow fever.

One of the most aggressive mosquitoes is the Asian tiger mosquito, *Aedes albopictus*, named for its white-barred body and white-spotted legs. It is a native of Southeast Asia, from southern India and China through Malaysia, Indonesia and the Philippines, and is a major vector for dengue fever. Dengue haemorrhagic fever is a debilitating viral disease, causing severe flu-like symptoms of high temperature and body aches, and can be fatal. Unlike malaria, which is predominantly a rural plague, dengue also occurs in urban centres, including many of the major cities of the Far East.

There was great consternation when *Aedes albopictus* was found in Texas in 1985. It has now spread along the eastern seaboard as far as Maine, and inland to Nebraska and Minnesota. The mosquitoes had not flown to the USA. The insect's spread has been brought about by the trade in secondhand car tyres, which are shipped across the globe to be reused or remoulded. Although relatively expensive to manufacture, tyres are cheap and easy to transport. They can be left for days or weeks on the warehouse lot, dockside or in the cargo hold, and they will not deteriorate or decay. They will, however, accumulate slops of rainwater, and it is in these artificial pools that the Asian tiger mosquito breeds.

Unknowingly, tyres, slops and mosquito larvae have been dragged all over the world. *Aedes albopictus* appeared in southern Italy in 1990 and has now reached South America and southern Africa. It will inevitably spread further.

Most embarrassing insect

NAME **crab louse** *Pthirus pubis*

LOCATION worldwide

ATTRIBUTE not spoken of in polite society

Lice are bloodsucking parasites and spend their entire lives firmly attached to their hosts – birds and mammals (except marsupials by a strange quirk of plate tectonics). Lice get about by crawling. They have massive muscular claws to grip the hair shafts (or feather plumules if they are bird lice) and they use them with great dexterity to move easily through the dense hair, fur or down to avoid the grooming of their victims. Contrary to popular myth, lice never move about on clothing, bedding, furniture, towels or toilet seats. If they ever leave the warm, humid protection of their host's hair, they die.

Crab lice get their name from their broad, squat form and huge claws. Only 2–3 mm (0.08–0.1 in) long, they are similar in size to the common head louse, *Pediculus capitis* (see page 272). Head lice are slim and adapted to the fine hairs on human heads. Crab lice have larger claws, adapted to the coarse and widely spaced hairs of the pubis, arm pits, hairy chests or beards.

With their blood food always available, all lice have to worry about is excreting too much water as a result of their wholly liquid diet. Runny droppings would soon clog their host's hair, making it more awkward for them to get about, and interfering with the delicate process of gluing their eggs (nits) to the base of individual hair strands. So lice evaporate the excess water directly through their skin and deposit dry dust grains of faecal material (nitty gritty). This makes them very vulnerable to desiccation if they are away from the moist skin surface for very long. So they don't let go. The only way they can transfer from one host to another is through direct physical contact. For crab lice this means intimate contact between lovers.

Most dangerous insect

NAME **malaria mosquitoes** in the genus *Anopheles*
LOCATION tropical Africa, Asia, Central and South America
ATTRIBUTE biggest killer of humans

Insects are small, but some can be very annoying. Ants bite, bees and wasps sting, head lice itch. These are but minor inconveniences, though, compared to the real danger presented by some insects – as vectors of disease. There are good grounds for suggesting that the common house fly, *Musca domestica*, was, until recently, the most dangerous animal on the planet. Breeding in filth, over 100 different pathogens have been isolated from it and 65 of them, including bacteria, helminth worms, protozoa and viruses, are known to be spread by it when it comes indoors to visit our food. The transmission of diseases such as dysentery, polio, typhoid, cholera, diphtheria and tuberculosis have also been blamed on the fly. The house fly is scarcer in the houses of the developed world today following sanitary reform in the 19th century and the arrival of the refrigerator.

Nevertheless, the insect menace still lurks. Four of the world's five most deadly diseases (malaria, leishmaniasis, sleeping sickness and lymphatic filariasis) are spread by insects. Of these, malaria, caused by a micro-organism called *Plasmodium*, is the greatest threat to human health. It is spread by mosquitoes.

The malarial life cycle starts when a female mosquito carrier takes a blood meal from a non-infected person. To prevent the human blood-clotting mechanism from blocking its slender tube-like mouthparts, the fly injects anticoagulant saliva to keep its meal free-flowing. This saliva is infected with the resting sporozoite (spore) stage of the disease. The sporozoites pass into the host's blood and infect the liver, where they transform into cells that rapidly duplicate themselves, releasing vast numbers of blood-circulating organisms called merozoites. These either reinfect the liver or invade the red blood cells, producing further huge numbers of merozoites. Malarial fever is the human immune reaction to the release of these alien bodies into the blood. Some of the infected blood cells inevitably get eaten by another mosquito, days or weeks later. Inside the fly's gut the male and female malarial parasites combine to create new sporozoites, ready to infect the next host.

Each year there are over 500 million cases of malaria worldwide. Approximately 1 million people die annually from it. Most of these are children in Sub-Saharan Africa.

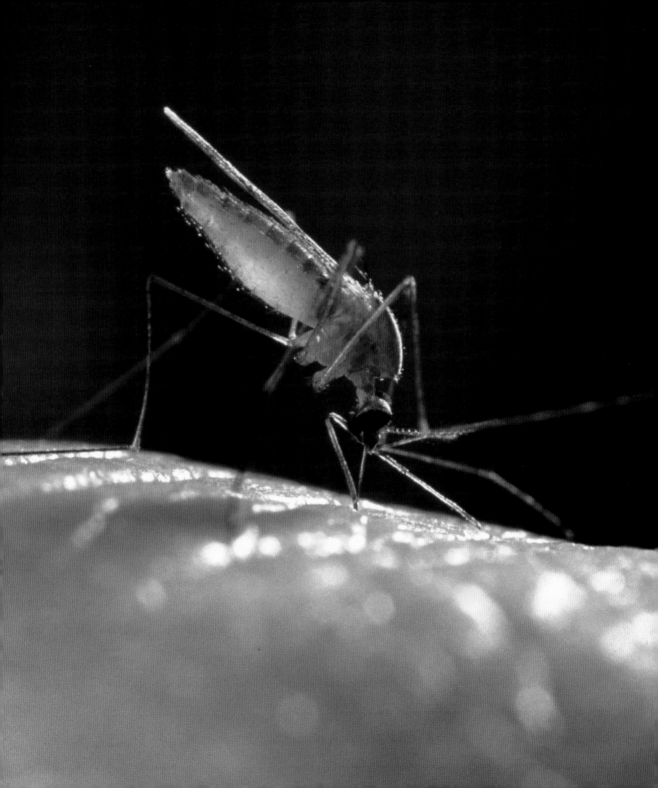

Most valuable service

NAME **honeybee** *Apis mellifera*
LOCATION worldwide
ATTRIBUTE pollination on an industrial scale

Although honey and beeswax are the most obvious material benefits from beekeeping, these are as nothing compared to the pollination of the world's crops carried out by honeybees. There is a tradition of placing hives in orchards when the trees are in blossom, because the bees are the best pollinators and make sure that the trees produce their best harvest.

Today the almond industry of California has arguably the largest movement of beehives in the world. The state's 250,000 hectares (600,000 acres) of almond monoculture orchards require nearly 150,000 hives to be shipped in on a fleet of lorries each February from all over the USA. Elsewhere itinerant beehives are delivered on site to pollinate apples, soft fruit and alfalfa (lucerne). An estimated 10–15 per cent of human food crops and a further 10–15 per cent of all animal feedstuffs are honeybee pollinated.

Pollen is the plant world's equivalent of sperm. In flowering plants it is transferred from the male parts of one flower to the female parts of another by a go-between. A few bats and birds perform this service, but most pollination is done by insects.

Honeybees (and to some extent bumblebees) are the supreme pollinators because they follow a policy of flower fidelity. Each bee, or sometimes a large group of bees from the hive, forages only on one species of flower at a time, moving from bloom to bloom of that flower on each forage trip, and not being distracted by other flower species nearby. This ensures good transfer of pollen from the male to female of that particular plant species without any wasteful scattering to the blooms of other plant species.

Pollen is a vital protein-rich food for the bees. They harvest it by raking their bodies with pollen combs on the back feet, which gather and press the soft, sticky pollen dust into a stiff paste carried on special bristles (called pollen baskets) on the back legs. But even the most meticulous bee still carries many thousands of pollen grains in its feathery hairs on to the next flower.

Most diverse insect fauna

LOCATION   Central America
ATTRIBUTE   richest and most diverse insect fauna on Earth

One of the greatest drivers of evolution is physical isolation. If a group of individuals of a particular species are separated from competitors, predators, parasites or diseases, they spread, invading new habitats and ecological niches. As they multiply, they adapt to the new territories available to them, evolving new shapes, forms, and behaviours often wildly different from those of the 'relatives' they left behind. Mountains, rivers, deserts and oceans are all major isolators.

The world's continents have not always been as spread out as they are now. About 250 million years ago there was only one large landmass, the supercontinent Pangaea. The drift of the geological surface plates that cover the Earth has been pulling this mass apart ever since. About 180 million years ago, Laurasia (North America, Europe and Asia) split away from Gondwana, which itself started to split into Africa, South America, India, Antarctica and Australia 150-140 million years ago. Recently (a few million years ago), the continents started to collide with each other. Tropical Africa is still separated from Europe by the Mediterranean (and the Sahara), and from Asia by the relatively arid Middle East. India and Asia met broadly, but the resulting Himalayas have created a new isolating barrier. Australia and Southeast Asia are not quite joined, and the string of Indonesian and other islands can be neatly separated by a line southwest of Borneo and Java where mostly Asian animals and plants meet mostly Australasian ones.

Only on the narrow isthmus of Central America do two of the great continents directly meet in tropical rainforest. Typically, tropical rainforests have the richest species diversity. Abundance of sunlight and water and the absence of any extreme temperature changes make them fertile and comfortable. Insects and other organisms thrive. When the land masses met, 3 million years ago, there were two great migrations north and south, passing each other here. An estimated 15-20 per cent of the world's 1 million recorded species of insects are thought to occur here, making this geographically small zone the species-richest place on the planet.

Mammalian blood is an especially valuable substance. As well as transporting dissolved gases and nutrients through the body of its rightful owner, it is particularly sought after by numerous blood-suckers for its nutrient richness and easy availability. Of these, flies are the most tiresome. Some, like horseflies and clegs, are large insects with stout mouthparts and suitably painful bite, but they are fairly easily detected as they drone in for the attack and rarely appear in large numbers. At the other end of the blood-sucking spectrum, malarial mosquitoes are life-threatening. Irritation is something altogether more subtle (and less perilous). It is a comparatively mild anger – the annoyance and frustration felt by those whose leisure enjoyment is interrupted by something as trivial as a cloud of flies.

The biting midges of the fly families Ceratopoginidae and Simuliidae are widely disliked for the biting clouds that drive those outside to seek sanctuary indoors. Their small size and large numbers make them difficult to dissuade. They get into the eyes, ears, nose and mouth, crawl up sleeves and trouser legs and down collars. They are active all day long and they occur throughout the developed world, which is where leisure activities are centred.

The midges come into conflict with humans when the female flies require a blood meal to mature their eggs, and are attracted to large, dark shapes giving off carbon dioxide. The humans they generally find are those working or holidaying in the wilderness and countryside. In parts of Canada and the USA in particular, midges have been blamed for postponing the start of the tourist season until mid-July, when weather and attractions are ready in early June.

Most irritating insect

NAME	**blackflies** in the family Simuliidae, and **biting midges** in the family Ceratopoginidae
LOCATION	worldwide, but especially noted in North America and Europe
ATTRIBUTE	annoying enough to cause serious financial loss to tourism

Most valuable insect product

NAME   **silk moth** *Bombyx mori*
LOCATION   origins in China, now worldwide
ABILITY   caterpillars produce silk thread, used to produce the most luxurious fabric in the world

Silk, a byword for luxury, wealth and expensive living, is the creation of lowly worms – silkworms, the caterpillars of the silk moth. This thoroughly domesticated insect is unknown in the wild, but is farmed on an industrial scale, mainly in the Far East. However, despite the economies brought by mass breeding, this is still a laborious and costly process.

Each female silk moth lays 350–500 eggs and the tiny hatchling larvae are fed on freshly harvested mulberry leaves, laid out on trays. After three weeks they are fully grown (about the size of your thumb) and start spinning the cocoons in which they will transform into adult moths.

It takes a caterpillar two or three days to wrap itself in a single silk thread, only 30 microns (thousandths of a millimetre) in diameter but up to 2,000 m (6,500 ft) long. Silk is a complex substance, which is produced by the caterpillar as a liquid, but immediately hardens on contact with air. An inner core of an elastic protein 'fibroin' is covered with a sticky gelatinous protein 'sericin', which acts as a natural glue to keep the mass of strands in place.

A few of the cocoons are kept to rear the next generation of adults, while the others are sorted for thread production. Immersing the cocoon in boiling water for a few minutes dissolves the sericin, and the cocoon begins to unravel. The ends of the strands are tied to spindles, and machines unwrap them to produce the raw silk ready for dyeing and weaving.

The origins of sericulture (silk production) are lost in the dark recesses of prehistory, but the first written records of it date from about 2600 BCE in China. According to legend, the Chinese empress Hsi Ling-Shi accidentally dropped a silk moth cocoon into a hot cup of tea, only for it to spill open into a single glossy filament.

The silkworm's food, the white mulberry (*Morus alba*), is native to China, and the Chinese jealously guarded, on pain of death, a monopoly in silk production for 2,500 years. In about 150 BCE, eggs were successfully smuggled to India and later to Persia and Turkey. Silk is now produced throughout the world, but the trade is still dominated by China and Japan.

Most medically useful insect

NAME **common greenbottle** *Lucilia (=Phaenicia) sericata*

LOCATION worldwide

ATTRIBUTE maggots used to clean festering and gangrenous wounds

Maggots are generally held in very low cultural esteem. They infest food, destroy crops, and are generally associated with dirt, dung, decay and detritus. Technically a maggot is a soft-bodied, legless, worm-like ('vermiform') insect larva. The word can be used with a certain amount of flexibility, but it is most often applied to the larvae of flies.

There are many recorded anecdotes about maggot infestations of human flesh. Maimed soldiers often lay where they fell on the battlefield for many days, and with the onset of infection and gangrene even minor injuries could be fatal. The French military surgeon Ambroise Paré reported that during the Battle of Saint Quentin, against the Spanish in 1557, many of the maggot-infested wounded recovered remarkably well. Similar observations were made during Napoleon's Egyptian Campaign, the Crimean War and the American Civil War. It seemed that the maggots ate the dead, dying (necrotic) and infected tissue, but left undamaged skin, muscle and sinew to heal.

Unfortunately maggot revulsion ran deep. With the discovery of microbes, and the 'germ' theory of illness and infection, the idea of deliberately putting contaminated objects into a wound went against all medical understanding and intuition. It was not until the 1920s that maggot cleaning of infected wounds started to become accepted. This procedure was short-lived, though: by the 1940s, the development of antibiotics had rendered maggots redundant.

With the appearance of antibiotic resistance in bacteria (MRSA, for example), doctors are now facing a fresh onslaught of infected wounds that fail to heal or develop severe infections, even gangrene. The stage is set for the humble maggot to make a reappearance. Sterile-reared *Lucilia* maggots are now widely available from medical suppliers to treat necrotic wounds.

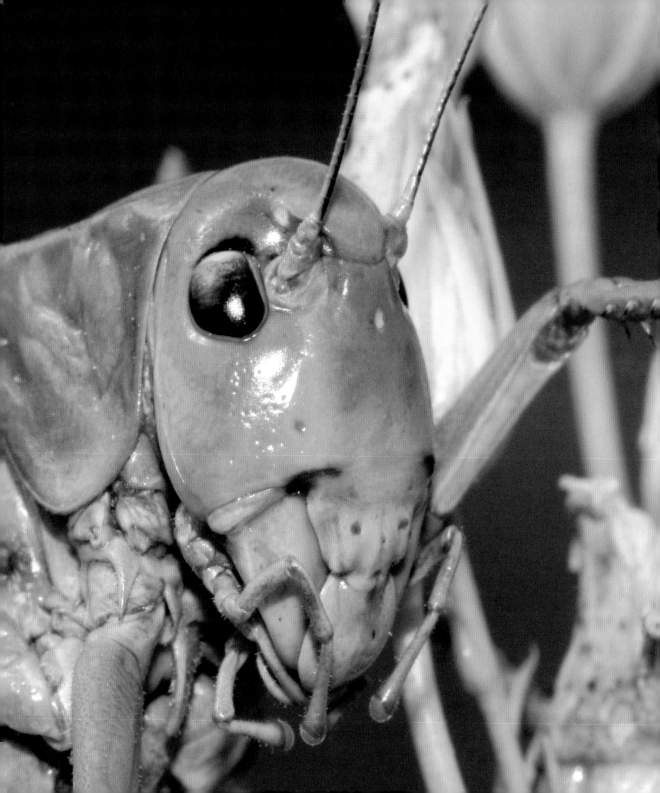

Most dermatologically useful insect

NAME **wart-biter** *Decticus verrucivorus*

LOCATION Europe and Asia

ATTRIBUTE used by humans to chew off warts

Many larger animals are named after their exploitation by humans: because they are eaten, their skin or fur is used, they are kept as pets or they are hunted for sport. Most insects, by contrast, are named for their nuisance factor. Horseflies pester horses for their blood, woodworms destroy timber, clothes-moths infest wardrobes and cabbage whites ravage the brassicas.

There are, however, a few insects that have acquired curious utilitarian status among humans, and none is more bizarre than a large green and brown speckled bush-cricket. Although grasshoppers (including locusts) are herbivores, using their short, tough jaws to chew plant material, the closely related bush-crickets are omnivorous and will eat small invertebrates, including grasshoppers given half the chance. This species may not be the largest bush-cricket in Europe, but its stout build has given it jaws powerful enough to break human skin, and which have found a use in the removal of warts, corns and other raised areas of toughened dermis.

In English this insect could go by no other name than the wart-biter. Elsewhere it is similarly named for its singular cosmetic purpose: *Warzenbeißer* (German), *vortebider* (Danish), *wrattenbijter* (Dutch), *vårtbitare* (Swedish). When the naturalist Linnaeus gave it a scientific name in 1758, he called it *Decticus verrucivorus*, which means verruca-eating.

According to the early entomologists who recorded such observations, it was German and Swedish peasants who first made use of the insect's surgical jaws to their dermatological advantage. One can imagine the eureka moment when a beaming peasant held up a large insect and bleeding finger and announced: 'Hey, that's just given me a brilliant idea.'

Most dramatic recovery from near-extinction

NAME   **Lord Howe Island stick insect** *Dryococelus australis*

LOCATION   Ball's Pyramid (and Melbourne Zoo)

ATTRIBUTE   thought extinct, rediscovered, may be reintroduced in the near future

In 1788, HMS *Supply*, under the command of Lieutenant Henry Lidgbird Ball, was on its way from Australia to Norfolk Island in the Pacific Ocean to establish a penal colony. Six hundred kilometres (400 miles) off the Australian coast, it came across a small, uninhabited, crescent-shaped island which was subsequently named Lord Howe Island.

Many strange creatures had evolved in this isolated paradise midway between Australia and New Zealand, none more peculiar than the Lord Howe Island stick insect, *Dryococelus australis*, a wingless insect 15 cm (6 in) long sometimes called the 'land lobster' for its resemblance to a crustacean.

It was not long before pigs and goats were deliberately released as livestock to supply passing ships with food, and in 1834 a settlement was established on the island. Inevitably this had a detrimental effect on the pristine wilderness, but the worst ecological disaster occurred in 1918 when the merchant ship *Makambo* ran aground and rats escaped. Along with several endemic bird species, the land lobster was thought to be extinct by 1930. However, in 2001 a team of ecologists landed on Ball's Pyramid, a sheer-sided rock pinnacle about 20 km (13 miles) to the southwest of the island, to survey wildlife on the treeless slopes of this volcanic sea stack. They were astonished to find a single Melaleuca bush sheltering 24 individuals of the long-thought-vanished stick insect.

The ecologists collected two males and two females – one pair for a private breeder and one pair for Melbourne Zoo. The captive breeding programme is now well under way, and by the end of 2008 the population had gone through four generations, there were several dozen breeding adults and many hundreds of eggs waiting to hatch. The time is ripe for a rat-eradication programme on Lord Howe Island, and the reintroduction of the land lobster to its former home.

Most forensic insect

NAME **bluebottle** *Calliphora vicina*

LOCATION North America, Europe, northern Asia

ATTRIBUTE accurate indicator of time of death

Faced with murder or a suspicious death, the first question a police officer must ask is not who, how or why, but when? This vital piece of information impacts on every part of the investigation. The onset of rigor mortis and the temperature of the corpse can be used to calculate up to a few hours after death, but bodies are sometimes not found for days or even weeks. Estimating the time since death of a decomposing corpse has to rely on other indicators – insects.

A corpse is a valuable source of protein, and large numbers of insects visit to lay their eggs. During the process of decay, a whole series of different insects feed on the body. Freshly dead bodies first attract blowflies and the beetle predators that feed on their maggots. After a few days, bacterial decay causes putrescent bloating, which brings in smaller decay-feeding flies. After two or three weeks, carrion beetles feed in the drying carcass. By two or three months, there is little left except hair, bones and a few hide beetles.

The commonest and most important insect indicator is the common bluebottle fly, *Calliphora vicina*. It arrives at a fresh corpse within hours and lays up to 300 eggs in mouth, nose, ears, eyes, skin crevices and any available wound orifices. The maggots hatch after about 24 hours and penetrate the flesh to feed. The rate at which the larvae feed depends on the ambient temperature, but they are usually fully grown in 14–25 days. As a larva feeds, it outgrows its skin, which splits and is cast off. This happens three times before the larva changes to pupa (chrysalis), then to final adult. Each of these stages has been well studied, so the presence of any of them on a corpse allows a backward calculation from discovery to when the first eggs were laid. This gives an accurate estimate of the time since death.

Throughout human history, head lice, *Pediculus capitis*, have been something of a scourge. They and their empty eggs cases (nits) are preserved in archaeological remains, as are the combs used to try to get rid of them. But we should be thankful. Head lice are a mild nuisance, but they pose no significant danger to health. Unlike many other blood-sucking insects (see page 254), head lice are not disease vectors.

Head lice are not indicators of uncleanliness, social unworthiness or ungodliness. There may still be shame attached to these annoying vermin, but this is not a rational feeling. Head lice can occur on anyone, irrespective of social class, upbringing, wealth, status or how many times a week hair is washed. In fact, head lice do better on clean hair than in dirty hair. They tend to get stuck in the natural oils that build up in lank, unwashed locks.

There was a time when health professionals worried about anaemia and blood loss associated with heavy louse infestation, but in 2005 accurate measurements of louse blood meals were calculated. Head lice were harvested from Australian schoolchildren, kept warm and moist in humane conditions, but starved, for 6–8 hours. They were weighed in batches, allowed to feed on the back of the scientists' hands for 15 minutes, then weighed again.

The blood sucked was minuscule. An adult female head louse drank 0.0001579 ml of blood; an adult male drank just 0.0000657 ml. These are not even pin pricks. Assuming a louse feeds between three and five times a day, a child would have to be on the very edge of anaemia already for this to make a difference. The highest infestation rate recorded is 2,657 lice on the head of a single child. Between them, they would rob a child of 0.7 ml of blood per day, a trivial amount.

Worst infestation of a person

NAME   **head louse** *Pediculus capitis*
LOCATION   Townsville, Australia
ATTRIBUTE   highest recorded infestation of a human

Best example of evolution in action

NAME **peppered moth** *Biston betularia*
LOCATION industrial Europe and North America
STATUS rapid evolution of a black form well hidden on soot-covered trees

Evolution by natural selection works on a very simple idea. Individuals of a given species are all slightly different. If a small difference in one individual helps its survival and mating ability, it will pass on the difference to its offspring, who in their turn are better able to survive and pass on the same genes. Over many generations, small differences can become increased until the new forms look very different from their long-past ancestors. Evolution in the wild normally occurs over thousands or millions of years. However, between 1848 and 1895, a rapid evolution took place in the peppered moth, *Biston betularia*, and it has become a textbook example of evolution in action.

The 'normal' moth (form *typica*) is a pale cream, peppered all over with dark speckles. It is perfectly camouflaged on the equally pale mottled bark of lichen-covered trees. In 1848 an all-black (melanic) form of the moth was found in Manchester, the heartland of Britain's new industrial urban areas. The form was named *carbonaria*. By 1895, 98 per cent of the peppered moths in the area were dark; form *typica* had all but disappeared. The same changes were occurring

elsewhere in the world: *carbonaria* appeared in Holland in 1867, and by 1900 was widespread across industrial Europe. A melanic form (*swettaria*) of the North American subspecies, *Biston betularia cognataria*, was found in 1906 near Philadelphia and soon spread throughout industrial Michigan and Illinois.

The reason for the change was believed to be that the black forms were better camouflaged against the cities' soot-covered trees (and thus better able to hide and survive), while the pale forms were so obvious that they were more likely to be found and eaten by predators. In a series of experiments during the 1950s, British entomologist Bernard Kettlewell set out to prove this theory. He released marked peppered moths of both forms into polluted and non-polluted woods. Form *carbonaria* fared better on the polluted blackened trees and form *typica* better on unpolluted lichened trees. With new antipollution laws, tree blackening with soot has declined in Britain, and the lichens are returning. So too the *carbonaria* form of the moth has decreased and the *typica* form has returned. The moth has evolved back to its former self.

Most endangered species

NAME   **American burying beetle** *Nicrophorus americanus*
LOCATION   Arkansas, Massachusetts, Nebraska, Oklahoma, Rhode Island and possibly South Dakota
STATUS   once widespread species now in population freefall

Though humans have been tormented by insects since times before history, those that make themselves so annoyingly obvious are a minuscule proportion of the vast numbers out there. Most insects are, by their nature, small, secretive and difficult to find. In order to study them, we have to search them out, and even in the best-researched regions of the world, there is still much we do not know about them.

It usually takes years or even decades of close observation to understand the life history of just a single species. Against this slow forward march of interpretation and understanding is the constant erosion of the natural environment by mankind's ill-considered exploitation. Often the gaining of some new insight into the natural world comes with the realisation that it is already being destroyed.

So it is with the American burying beetle, *Nicrophorus americanus*. It was once very widespread across the eastern USA and parts of southeast Canada, where it bred on the carcases of small animals. Its decline appears to have started during the 1920s, and by 1960 it had gone from all of its former range east of the Appalachians. It is now restricted to scattered colonies on the margins of its old territory. Some of these populations are only a few hundred individuals, and are probably not viable in the long term.

The major factor in the beetle's downturn was fragmentation of the habitat through urban development and the industrialisation of agriculture. It was not the beetle's dependence on particular carrion, or a specific type of lost habitat, that caused its disappearance (it occurred in prairie, scrubland, open woodland and deep forests), but as the islands of habitat became smaller, they were invaded by edge-dwelling scavengers such as skunks, opossums and racoons, which take carrion before the beetles can bury it and lay their eggs.

Did anyone see this fall coming? Not until late on. Despite its relatively large size (30 mm; 1¼ in) and handsome colours, the beetle is still 'just' an insect. It lacks the cuddliness of Madagascar's endangered lemurs or the powerful majesty of Siberian tigers, and its small size and secretive nature made it difficult to observe or study until … it may yet be too late.

Most destructive insect

The stone age, a period of prehistory going back about 3 million years, is so named because stone artefacts have been discovered from that time. But those early humans did not live in stone houses, sit on stone chairs or walk on stone roads. Like us today they would have used wood. Nothing of timber, however, remains. It has been destroyed.

In the tropics today, termites are probably the insects most destructive of timber structures, but they are absent from many parts of the world. Wood-boring beetles, however, are everywhere, and nothing escapes their depredations.

The short, fat grubs known as woodworms occur in virtually every type of timber known. The adult insects are beetles. Several groups are involved, but prominent are the furniture beetles (family Anobiidae), barkbeetles (Scolytidae), longhorns (Cerambycidae) and powderpost beetles (Bostrychidae). Before humans came along, they and a host of other dead-wood feeders, performed the important task of recycling the tough cellulose fibres that give tree trunks their immense strength. When humans harnessed this strong, flexible, material to make their houses, tools, furniture, weapons and so on, the beetles followed the timber indoors and continued chewing.

Timber is still a useful building material, but it is no accident that the great symbolic buildings of the present and the past are made of impervious stone, built to withstand attack from all quarters, but mainly from tiny wood-boring insects. Woodworms not only eradicate buildings. Since paper is also made of wood fibres, they are quite happy to eat that too. Bookworms are the same insects making a meal of printed books, illuminated manuscripts, papyri and wood-bark scrolls, removing art, knowledge, wisdom and poetry, too.

NAME	**woodworms** various beetles in the family Anobiidae and others
LOCATION	worldwide
ATTRIBUTE	destruction of timber buildings since prehistory

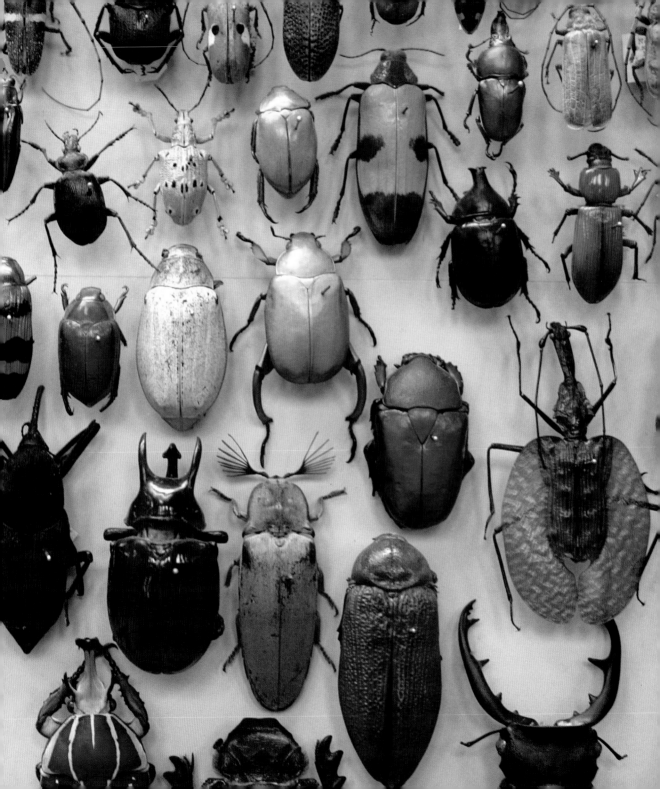

Most diverse group

NAME **beetles** in the order Coleoptera

LOCATION worldwide (everywhere except the polar regions) from seashore to mountaintop

ATTRIBUTE more different species than most other animals put together

The British scientist J.B.S. Haldane (1892–1964) was one reputedly asked by 'some solemn ass' what could be 'inferred of the mind of the Creator from a study of the works of Creation'. 'An inordinate fondness for beetles' was his equally reputed reply.

Towards the end of the 20th century, the number of insect species was estimated by examining specimens housed in the world's museums and private collections, descriptions of which had been published in the entomological literature since 1758, when Linnaeus's system of scientific names was adopted by the world's scientists. By 1980 about 1.2 million animal species were known. One million of these were insects, of which 400,000 were beetles with their characteristic hardened forewings.

In the last 30 years, entomologists have started to study tropical rainforest trees more keenly, and the number of known (and anticipated) species has had to be dramatically revised. The field technique was simple – an insecticide fogging machine was hauled up on ropes into the rainforest canopy, where it knocked down onto collection sheets below vast numbers of insects previously unknown to science.

The theoretical work back in the laboratory was slightly more complicated. Although some insects feed on a wide variety of food-plants, many are so specific that they will eat only one type of leaf, or leaves from a small and closely related group of plants. It was now possible to work out how many insect species there might be in the world using the number of insect species newly discovered by fogging and the number of known plant and tree species (plants were always better studied than animals because they do not run or fly away).

Extrapolating the data led to the suggestion that there were, perhaps, 30 million species out there (that would make 12 million types of beetle). Other researchers re-interpreted the numbers, but instead of reaching a consensus, further confusion reigns. Current estimates of insect diversity lie somewhere between 3 and 85 million species (with 1 to 30 million types of beetle). Whatever the number, it is feared that most of them will be extinct before they are described.

Rarest insect

NAME (just one of very many species) **duke water beetle** *Megadytes ducalis*

LOCATION Brazil

STATUS known from only one specimen, then never seen again

In 1882, distinguished British entomologist David Sharp (1840–1922) published his extensive monograph *On Aquatic Carnivorous Coleoptera, or Dytiscidae*, covering the water beetles of the world known at that time. Among several species described in the book that were new to science, he named one *Megadytes ducalis*, on account of its impressive size, nearly 50 mm (2 in) long and 30 mm (1⅕ in) wide. It is still the largest water beetle ever found.

In the usual fashion of the day, he described it in both Latin and English, gave its locality (Brazil) and the name of the collector (Saunders). In the concise 200-word entry for this species he also states: 'I have seen only a single individual of this species.' That single individual, now housed in the Natural History Museum, London, remains the only specimen ever found. Is this the rarest insect in the world?

For the vast majority of the 1 million or so insect species found in difficult and inaccessible parts of the planet, most of what we know about them comes from specimens housed in the world's museums and scientific institutions.

These have been collected piecemeal over the last 300 years, and studied when experts like Sharp have had the time or inclination to examine, identify and classify them. All too often, a new species is identified, described and published in the scientific literature with a comment like Sharp's: known only from a single unique specimen.

None of these many unique specimens can really be singled out as the rarest species, but *Megadytes ducalis* is an impressive beast and certainly worthy as a figurehead. In fitting with the styles of the time, the data label attached to the specimen offers the same meagre locality information as Sharp's monograph. Brazil is the fifth largest country in the world, with an area of 8.5 million sq km (3.3 million sq miles) and the largest freshwater system of rivers on Earth. The story goes that the specimen was found in the bottom of a dugout canoe.

How is it possible to go back and rediscover it now? All we can do is wait and see whether any more turn up. We may have to wait some time. In 1994, *Megadytes ducalis* was officially listed as extinct.

Index

Page numbers in *italic* refer
to illustrations

Acherontia atropos 232, 233
Acrocinus longimanus 172, 173
Actias 86, 87
Adalia decempunctata 44, 45
Aedes albopictus 250, 251
Africa 168, 175, 183, 241
    Central 99
    East 288
    North 38, 194, 225, 274
    Southern 41
    sub-Saharan 123, 144, 179
    tropical 198, 254
Alucita 32, 33
Amauris
    albimaculata 168
    niavius 168
America, tropical 198
Anax junius 166, 167
Angraecum sesquipedale 99
Anobiidae 279
Anolis 76
Anopheles 254, 255
Anostostomatidae 181
ant-house plants 124, 125
ant-nest flies 230, 231
Antarctica 155
Antarctophthirus
    microchir 155
    ogmorhini 154, 155
Anthrenus verbasci 163, 207, 236
antlions 136, 137
ants 109, 136, 183, 208, 219
    bullet 218, 219
    carpenter 22, 23

common black pavement 176, 177
    honeypot 28, 29
    leafcutter 128, 129
        minims 132, 133
    Sahara desert 194-5
    trap-jaw 70, 71
    weaver 122, 123
Apatura iris 162, 163
Apis mellifera 138, 139, 202, 256,
    257
Arabia, southern 168
Arachnocampa 156, 157
Araschnia levana 30, 31
Argentina 60, 172
Arixenia 193
Asia 38, 80, 100, 104, 183, 267
    central 47
    east 87
    northern 59, 153, 163, 177, 203,
        207, 238, 271
    Southeast 17, 35, 41, 123, 125,
        193
    tropical 198, 254
Atlantic Ocean 150
Atta 128, 129, 132, 133
    sexdens 128
Attacus atlas 63
Australia 28, 97, 103, 123, 125, 156,
    183, 225, 249
    eastern 246
    tropical 198

Ball's Pyramid 268
Batchian (Bacan) 48
batflies 198, 199
batwigs 192, 193
bedeguar 140, 141
bee-flies 56
bees 183, 219
    bumblebees 80, 81
    carpenter 108, 109
    honeybees 109, 138, 139, 208,
        212, 219, 256, 257
    sweat 219
beetles 280, 281
    African arrow-poison 82, 83
    American burying 276, 277
    bloody-nosed 46, 47
    bombadier 188, 189
    burying 134, 135, 276, 277
    carrion 271
    cigarette 163

    click 203
    cobweb 206, 207
    Colorado 226, 227
    Darwin's (Grant's) 60, 61
    death-watch 222, 223
    diving 112, 113
    duke water 282, 283
    dung 249
    elephant 12
    European snail 24, 25
    European stag 242, 243
    fire-flies 42
    furniture 279
    Ghost 16, 17
    glow-worms 24, 42
    golden jewel 200, 201
    Goliath 12
    Grant's (Darwin's) stag 60, 61
    ground 35, 83, 112
    harlequin 172, 173
    hedgehog leaf 110, 111
    Jamaican fire 42, 43
    leaf 112
    lily 184, 185
    longhorns 279
    museum 163, 207, 236
    Namib darkling 146-7, 146-7
    oil 164, 165
    powderpost 279
    scarab 220, 221
    Spanish fly 228, 229
    spider 163
    stag 242, 243
    tiger 96, 97, 149
    violin 34, 35
    water 112, 113
    water pennies 52, 53
    whirligig 120, 121
    wings 33
    wood-boring 279
bilateral gynandromorph 26, 27
bioluminescence 42
Biston betularis 274, 275
blackflies 261
blowflies 135, 271
bluebottle 270, 271
Bombus 80, 81
Bombyx mori 262, 263
bookworms 279
Borneo 14
Bostrychidae 279
bots, deer 95

Botswana 83
Brachinus 188, 188
Brazil 12, 282
Brevisana brevis 55
bugs 111
    spittle 202, 203
    true 42
bumblebees 80, 81
Buprestis aurulenta 200, 201
bush flies 248, 249
bush-crickets 111, 244, 245
    wart-biter 266, 267
butterflies
    African mocker swallowtail 168,
        169
    Albin's Hampstead eye 234, 235
    Apollo 158, 159
    Bath white 236
    bilateral gynandromorphs 26, 27
    brimstone 234
    brown hairstreak 234
    cabbage whites 17
    friar 168
    glasswing 66, 67
    Layman 168
    map 30, 31
    marsh fritillary 26, 27
    meadow argus 234, 235
    monarch 95, 168, 170, 171, 288
    orange oakleaf 64, 65
    owl 76, 77
    painted lady 212, 213
    Plukenet's collection 236, 237
    purple emperor 162, 163
    Wallace's golden birdwing 48,
        49

Cactoblastis cactorum 246-7, 246-7
Caligo 76, 77
Calliphora vicina 270, 271
Callistege mi 238, 239
camouflage 64
Camponotus inflatus 28
Campsocleis gratiosa 245
Carabidae 35
Cataglyphis bicolor 194-5, 194-5
caterpillars, lobster moth 58, 59
Central America 18, 42, 63, 71, 114,
    167, 225, 254
    insect fauna 258, 259
Cephenomyia pratti 95
Cerambycidae 279

Ceratitis capitata 205
Ceratoconcha schulzei 230
Ceratopogonidae 261
chafers, golden 18, 19
Chiasognathus granti 60, 61
Chile 60
China 64, 245, 262
Chrysididae 85
cicadas
    dog day 54, 55
    periodical 118, 119
Cicindela 149
Clemellis pullata 106, 107
Coccinella septempunctata 126
Coccus 230
Cochilomyia hominivorax 240, 241
cochineal 224, 225, 247
cockroaches 97, 112
coffin flies 197
Coleoptera 280, 281
Collembola 79
Colobopsis truncatus 22, 23
Colombia 12
colours 18
Conepteryx rhamni 234
Cooloola monsters 102, 103
Cooloola propator 102, 103
Cossus cossus 100–1, 100–1
crickets 55, 244, 245
    golden bell 245
    hump-winged 130, 131
    mole 88–9, 88–9
    singing brother 245
    snowy tree 142, 143
    thermometer 143
    weaving lady 245
Ctesias serra 206, 207
cuckoo spit 203
Cynthia
    cardui 212, 213
    hampstediensis 234
Cyphocilus 16, 17
Cyphoderris 130, 131

Dactylopius coccus 224, 225
Danaus
    chrysippus 168
    plexippus 170, 171
dance flies 68, 69
Daphnia 79
darner, common green 166, 167
Decticus verrucivorus 266, 267

Deinacrida heteracantha 92, 93
Diamphidia 83
diamphotoxin 83
Dicopomorpha echmepterygis 90, 91, 106
dimorphism 30
Diopsidae 41
Diplolepis rosae 140, 141
Dismorphia 168
Dolania americana 187
dragonflies 95
    common green darner 166, 167
    darter 210, 211
    globe skimmer 288
Drilus flavescens 24, 25
Drosophila
    bifurca 190, 191
    melanogaster 216, 217
Dryococelus australis 268, 269
Dytiscidae 112

earwigs, parasitic 192, 193
Echmepteryx hageni 91
Ecuador 12
Ephemeroptera 33, 187
Eumenidae 160
Euphydryas aurinia 26, 27
Europe 24, 30, 38, 47, 59, 80, 100, 104, 143, 153, 163, 177, 203, 207, 229, 238, 242, 267, 271, 274
    western 36
eyes 73, 167

fire-flies 42
fleas 203, 208, 209, 212
    water 79
flies
    ant-nest 230, 231
    big-headed 56, 57
    bush 248, 249
    coffin 197
    dance 68, 69
    fruit 204, 205, 216, 217
    horse 72, 73
    house 254
    New World screw-worm 240, 241
    ox warble 152, 153
    parasitoid 106, 107
    scuttle 196, 197
    stalk-eyed 40, 41

tsetse 178, 179
Forcipomyia 104, 105
froghopper 202, 203, 288
fruit flies 204, 205, 216, 217
fungus gnat larvae 20, 21

gad-flies 153
Ghost beetles 16, 17
Glossina 178, 179
glow-worms 24, 42
    Australian 156, 157
Goliathus
    goliathus 12
    regius 12
grasshoppers 55, 143, 203
greenbottle, common 264, 265
Gryllidae 245
Gryllotalpa 88–9, 88–9
Guianas 12
gynandromorphs 26, 27
Gyrinus 120, 121

Halobates 150, 151
    sobrinus 150
Heliconius 168
Hexapoda 10
Hipparchia hampstediensis 234
Hippodamia convergens 126, 127
Hispa 110, 111
Hispella 110, 111
Homallotermes 71
honeybees 109, 138, 139, 208, 212, 219, 256, 257
hornet, European 219
horntails 38
hornworms 95
    tobacco 95
horse flies 72, 73
house flies 254
hoverflies 56
Hydrometra 78, 79
Hypoderma bovis 152, 153
Hypoponera punctatissima 167

ichneumon, sabre 38, 39
India, northern 64
India, southern 288
Indian Ocean 150, 288
Indonesia 48
Iridiomyrmex cordatus 124, 125
Ischnomantis gigas 114
Issus coleoptratus 288

Japan 64, 245
Junonia villida 234, 235
Kallima inachus 64, 65
katydids 55, 143, 245
Keroplatidae 21

lacewings, eggs 74, 75
ladybirds
    convergent 126, 127
    ten-spot 44, 45
Lasioderma serricorne 163
Lasius niger 176, 177
leaf bugs 101
leafhopper bugs 37
Lebistina 83
Lepisma saccharina 163
Leptinotarsa decimlineata 226, 227
Leptonychotes weddellii 155
lice 208, 212
    bark 91
    crab 252, 253
    head 253, 272, 273
    Weddell seal 155
light generation 42
Lilioceris
    lilii 184, 185
    merdigera 184
lizards 76
locusts 95
    desert 174, 175
Lucanus cervus 242, 243
Lucilia sericata 264, 265
Lyonetia clerkella 36–7, 36–7
Lyssa vesicatoria 228, 229

Macromantis hyalina 114, 115
Macrotermes 144, 145
    michaelseni 144
Madagascar 50, 99, 168
Magicicada septendecim 118, 119
Maldives 288
Manduca sexta 95
mantids 131
    giant 114, 115
mayflies 33, 186, 187
    sandburrowing 187
Mecopoda elongata 245
Mediterranean 232
Megadytes ducalis 282, 283
Meganeura monyi 63
Meganeuropsis permiana 63

Megasoma
  actaeon 12
  elephas 12
Meloidae 164
Methoca articulata 148, 149
Mexico 28, 172, 288
Microdon 230, 231
Middle East 232
midges, biting 104, 105, 261
mimicry 168
Morgan's sphinx 98, 99
Mormolyce 34, 35
mosquitoes
  Asian 'tiger' 250, 251
  malaria 254, 255
moths
  apple-leaf miner 36-7, 36-7
  Atlas 63
  cactus 246-7, 246-7
  clearwings 67
  codling 106
  death's head hawkmoth 232, 233
  ghost 62, 63
  goat 100-1, 100-1
  hawkmoths 56, 94, 95, 99, 232, 233
  moon 86, 87
  Morgan's sphinx 98, 99
  Mother Shipton 238, 239
  peppered 274, 275
  silk 262, 263
  tobacco hornworm 95
  twenty-plumed 32, 33
  white witch 62, 63
mucus 21
Musca
  domestica 254
  vetutissima 248, 249
Mymaridae 91
Myrmecocystus 28
Myrmecodia 124, 125
Myrmeleon 136, 137

Namibia 83, 146
Neodohrniphora 132
neuston 79
New Guinea 28
New Zealand 93, 156, 181
Nicrophorus 134, 135
  americanus 276, 277
Niptus hololeucus 163

North America 38, 55, 80, 104, 126, 131, 143, 153, 167, 171, 177, 191, 201, 203, 226, 271
  eastern 68, 118
Odontomachus bauri 70, 71
Oecanthus
  fultoni 142, 143
  rileyi 143
Oecophylla 122, 123
  longinoda 123
  smaragdina 123
Opuntia 247
Ornithoptera croesus 48, 49
ox warble fly 152, 153

Pacific Ocean 150
Pantala flavescens 288
Papilio dardanus 168, 169
Paraponera clavata 218, 219
Parmula cocciformis 230
Parnassius 158, 159
Pediculus capitis 253, 272, 273
Periplaneta americana 97
Peru 12
Phaenicia sericata 264, 265
Pharnacia kirbyi 14
Philaenus spumarius 202, 203, 288
Phobaeticus
  chani 14, 15
  kirbyi 14
  serratipes 14
Phoridae 197
phorids 196, 197
Pieris 17
Pipunculidae 56
Plecoptera 33
Plukenet, Leonard, butterfly collection 236, 237
Plusiotes 18, 19
poisons 83
Polyclada 83
Pontia daplidice 236
Psephenidae 52
Pthirus pubis 252, 253
Pyrophorus noctilucus 42, 43

Queensland 103

Rhamphomyia longicauda 68, 69
Rhaphidophoridae 181
Rhyniella praecursor 10
Rhyniognatha hirsti 10, 11

Rhyssa 38, 39
Rivacicindela 96, 97
  hudsoni 97
robin's pin-cushion 140, 141

Scarabaeidae 221
Scarabaeus sacra 221
scarabs 220, 221
Schistocerca gregaria 174, 175
Scolytidae 279
Scotland 10
screw-worm, New World 240, 241
Scutelligera ammerlandia 230
scuttle flies 196, 197
sea-skaters 150, 151
seals, Weddell 155
Seychelles 288
shieldbugs 101
silverfish 163
Simuliidae 261
Siphonaptera 208, 209
smell 101
snail beetle, European 24, 25
South Africa 28
South America 12, 18, 42, 63, 71, 76, 114, 172, 225, 254
  Andean 80
Spain 225
Spanish fly 228, 229
sphinx moths 95
spittle bug 202, 203, 288
springtails 10, 42
Sphingidae 95
Stauropus fagi 59
Stenocara 146-7, 146-7
stick insects 14
  Lord Howe Island 268, 269
stoneflies 33
Streblidae 198
Svistella bifasciata 245
Sympetrum 210, 211
Syrex 38

Tabanidae 73
Tachnidae 106
Tephritidae 205
Termes 71
termites 71, 109, 144, 145
  higher 182, 183
Termitidae 183
Termitomyces 144

Tettigoniidae 245
Thecla betulae 234
Thysania agrippina 62, 63
Tibicen pronotalis 54, 55
Timarcha tenebricosae 46, 47
Titanus giganteus 12, 13
Trachelephorus giraffa 50, 51
trochanter 35
tsetse flies 178, 179

United Kingdom 238
United States 91, 276
  Western 28

Venezuela 12
Vespa crabro 219

walking insects 14
Wallace, Alfred Russel 48
wart-biter 266, 267
wasps 109, 183, 219
  cuckoo 85
  fairy 90, 91
  potter 160, 161
  rubytail 84, 85
water beetles 112, 113
  duke 282, 283
water measurers 78, 79
water pennies 52, 53
wedge-pushing 35
weevils
  giraffe-necked 50, 51
  leaf-milling 50
wetas 180, 181
  giant 92, 93
wings 87
woodworm 278, 279
  death-watch beetle 222, 223

Xanthopan morganii 98, 99
Xeniaria 193
Xestobium rufavillosum 222, 223
Xylocopa 108, 109
  auripennis 109